ENGLISH PRACTICE AND PROGRESS

GAMES

EDITED BY
JANE MYLES

SCHOLASTIC

MARY GLASGOW MAGAZINES

Contents

Colours

Read the words and colour the picture.

My favourite colour

My favourite colour is:

Here is my favourite colour:

Chase the Cheetah!

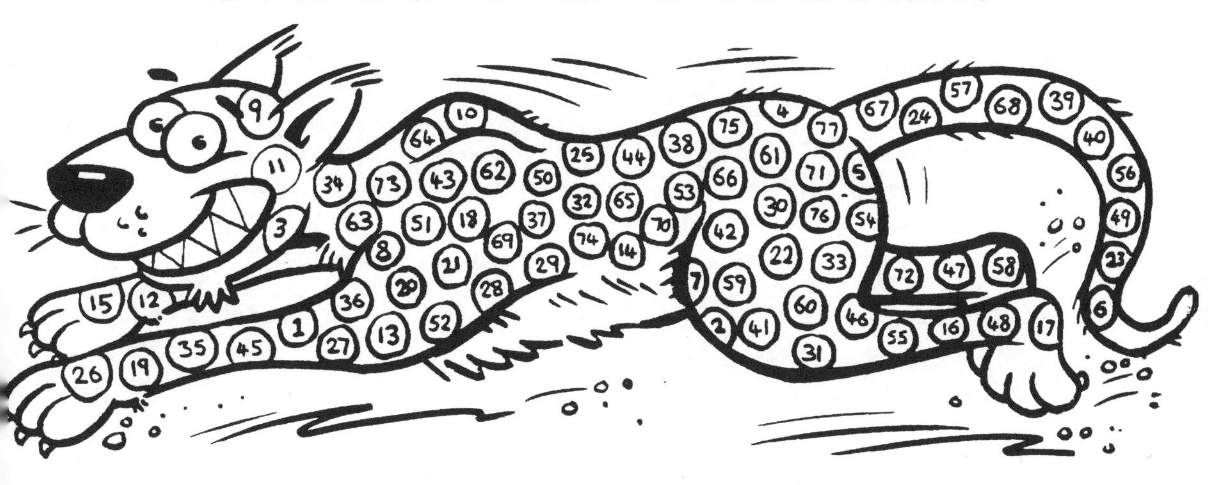

How fast can a cheetah run?

Colour the numbers from seven to ten.

Colour the numbers from twelve to twenty-three.

Colour the numbers from twenty-five to thirty-one.

Colour all the numbers over thirty-three.

Now add all the other numbers together.

Write:

A cheetah can run at .... km per hour.

Make a Word

The Colour Circle

r w e n d g p r i e n y k c b r l e a a c m k g w r h e i e t n e o y r e a l u l g o e w b d l u n r e p b l r e o

Go round the circle this way → write alternative letters in the centre of the circle ←

START HERE

1. How many colours can you find?

Write: 1. red 2. ....

....

....

....

....

....

....

....

....

....

....

2. Fill the spaces with names of colours or the words *darker* or *lighter*.

1. Grey is .... than .... but it's .... than black.

2. Pink is .... than red but it's .... than white.

3. Orange is .... than brown but it's .... than yellow.

4. Cream is .... than white but it's .... than yellow.

5. You mix .... and .... to make green.

6. You mix .... and red to make orange. You mix red and .... to make pink.

How many cats can you find?

Numbers and Colours

Can you find the numbers from 1-12 in this puzzle? The words can go

X	M	O	Q	T	W	O	F	I	C	E
R	B	N	L	U	J	V	O	X	T	L
P	E	I	G	H	T	P	M	W	R	O
K	D	N	B	I	H	C	N	U	M	W
H	O	E	U	M	U	Y	O	E	S	L
F	N	C	L	P	X	Q	F	R	T	E
R	S	E	I	E	T	I	N	D	H	V
U	T	G	V	S	V	R	S	F	R	L
O	P	I	M	E	F	E	K	B	E	E
F	N	Y	I	J	S	T	N	D	E	W
W	L	E	F	O	S	N	G	E	L	T

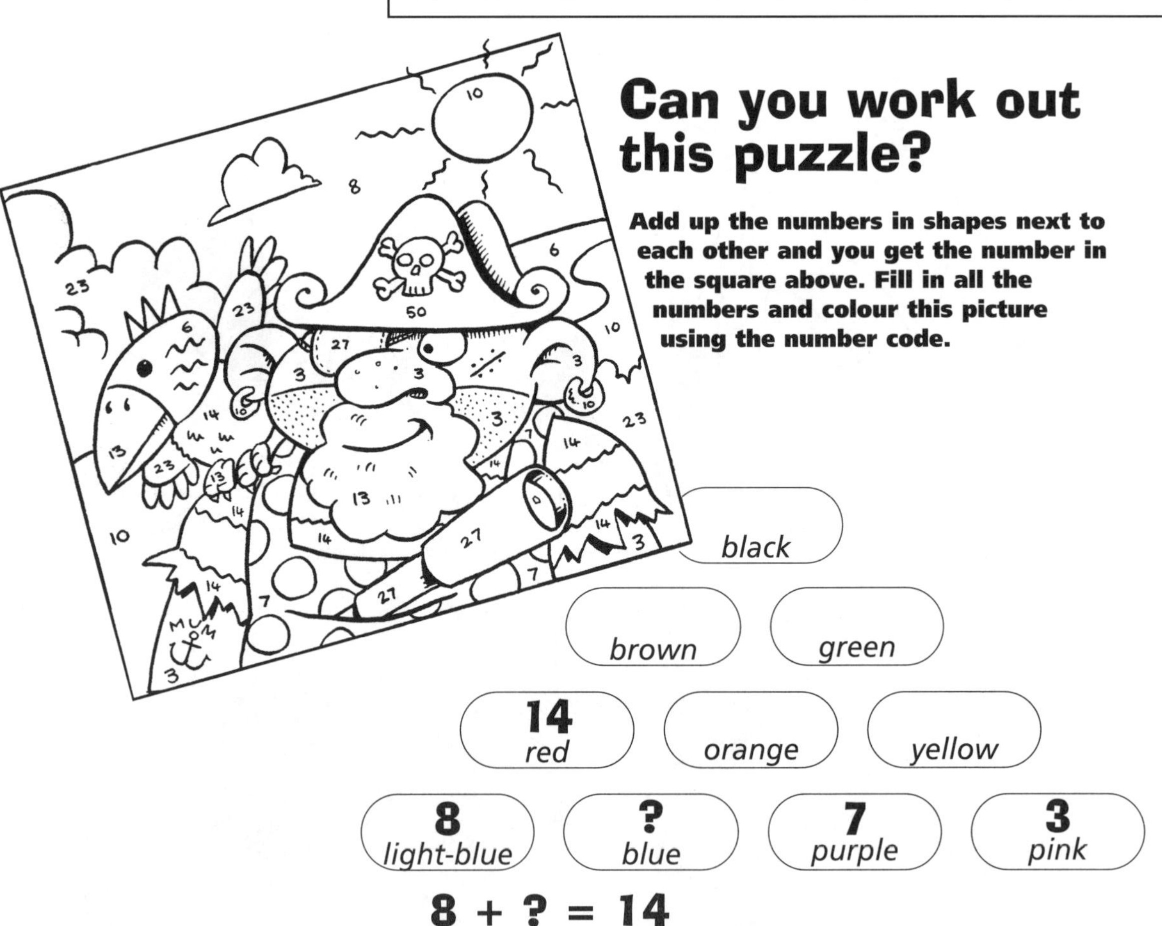

Can you work out this puzzle?

Add up the numbers in shapes next to each other and you get the number in the square above. Fill in all the numbers and colour this picture using the number code.

black

brown *green*

14 *red* *orange* *yellow*

8 *light-blue* **?** *blue* **7** *purple* **3** *pink*

8 + ? = 14

Find the Treasure

SECRET CODE BOOK

one = A	ten = I
three = O	eleven = N
four = D	twelve = E
five = B	thirteen = R
seven = S	fourteen = T
eight = H	fifteen = W
nine = U	

14-8-12 14-13-12-1-7-9-13-12 10-7 9-11-4-12-13 14-8-12 5-3-1-14 5-12-14-15-12-12-11 14-8-12 14-13-12-12-7

Where is the treasure?

Write the answer here:

....

....

....

....

....

....

....

.... **and draw an arrow on the picture.**

Weekend Plans

What do all these people want to do at the weekend? Can you do this puzzle? Work out the maths and find the right letters on the wheel. Can you spell the words?

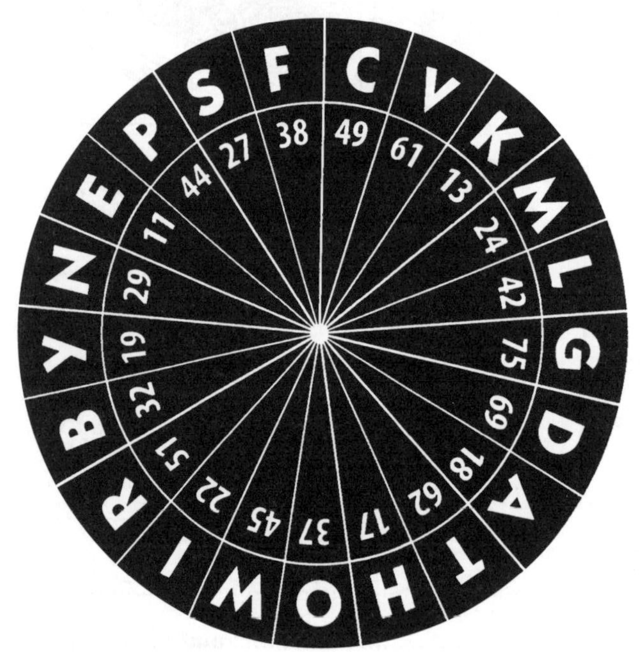

1. Let's go

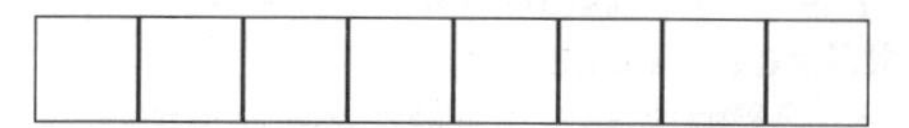

Subtract 6 from each of these numbers:
33, 51, 28, 30, 30, 28, 35, 81

2. How about going ☐☐☐☐☐☐☐ ?

Add 7 to each of the numbers
42, 12, 42, 35, 15, 22, 68

3. What about going ☐☐☐☐☐☐☐☐ ?

Divide each of these numbers by 2
54, 34, 74, 88, 88, 44, 58, 150

4. Why don't we watch a ☐☐☐☐☐ ?

Subtract 11 from these numbers
72, 33, 80, 22, 48

5. Let's play ☐☐☐☐☐☐☐☐

Add 9 to these numbers
29, 28, 28, 53, 23, 9, 33, 33

6. Why don't we go to the ☐☐☐☐ ?

Divide these numbers by 2
88, 36, 102, 26

The Mystery Ship

This is a famous English ship.
It is in Portsmouth.
What is it called?
Find the letters with the pictures.

_____ _____ _____
cat eight ship

_____ _____ _____ _____
teapot chair photo pizza

_____ _____ _____ _____
mountains three sea house

 T	 L	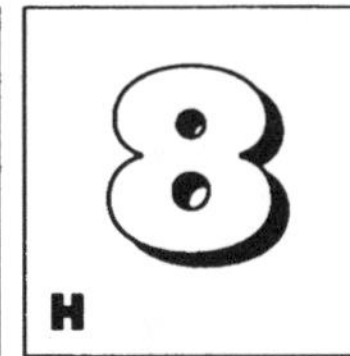 H	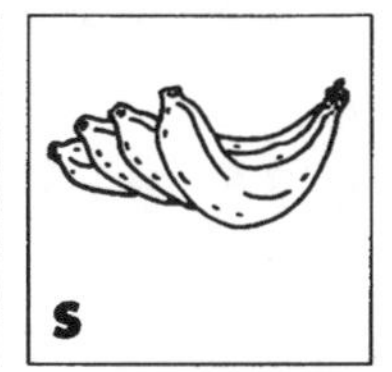 S	 P	 E
 M	 D	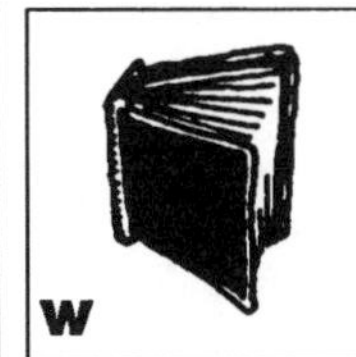 W	 N	 W	 G
 I	 A	 F	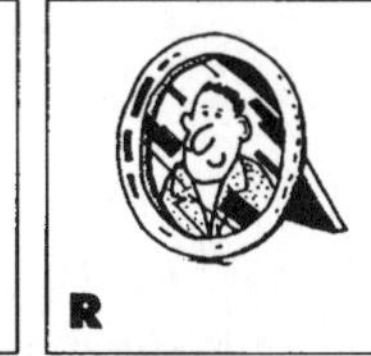 R	 Y	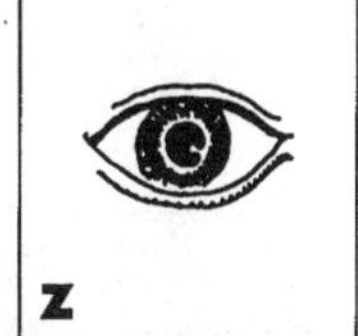 Z
 Q	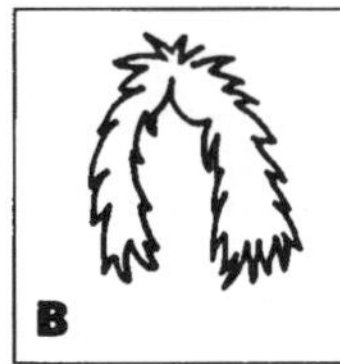 B	 R	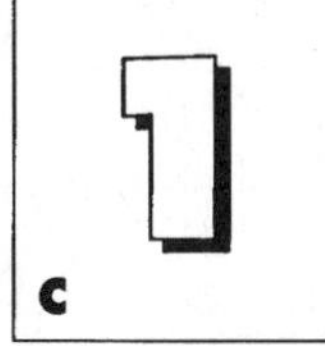 C	 U	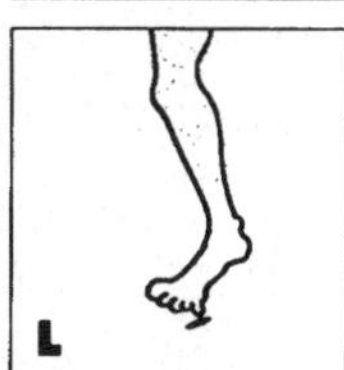 L
 K	 O	 V	 S	 E	 J

Make a Sentence

How many sentences can you make?

The Mystery Picture

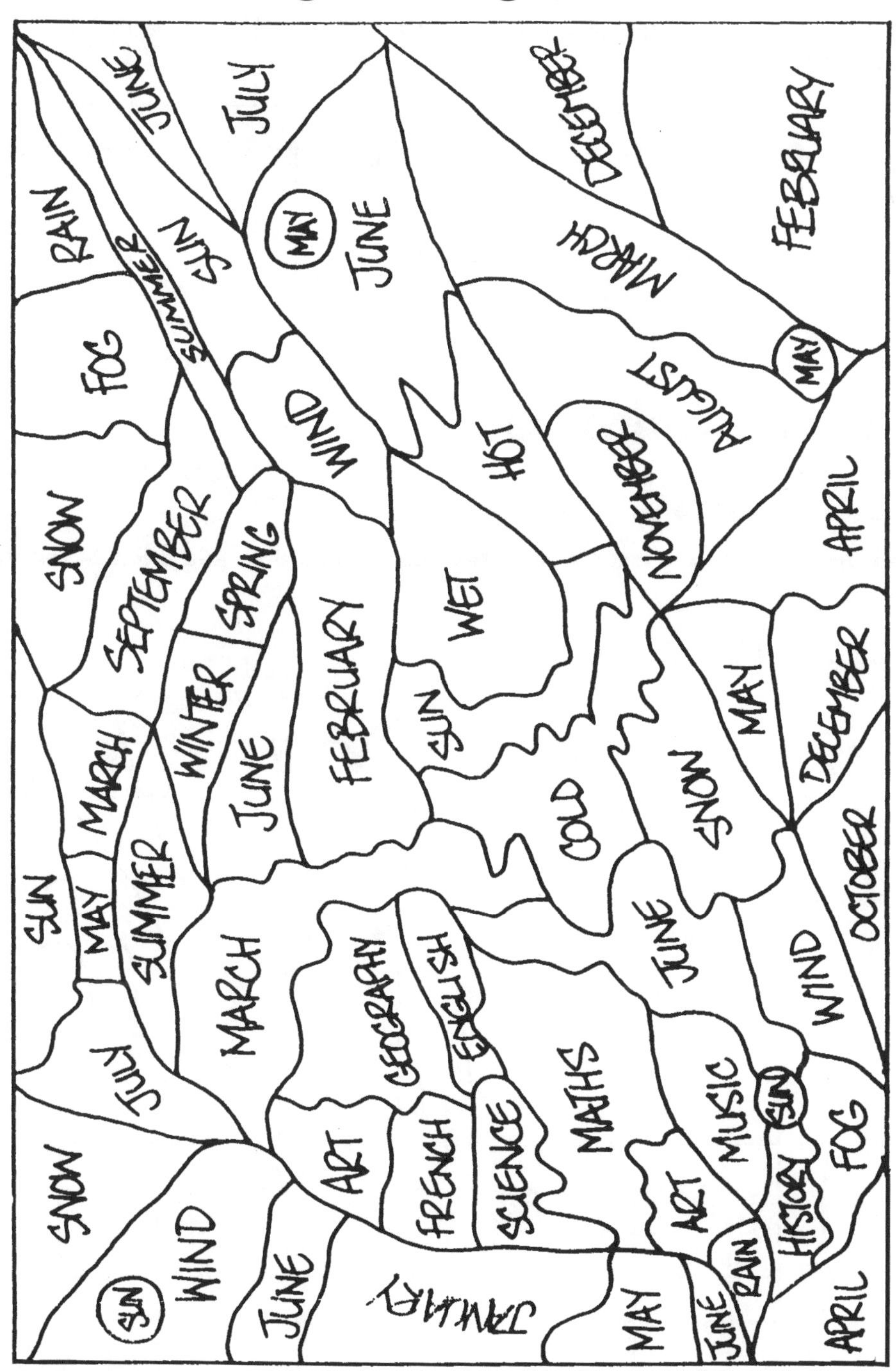

Colour the weather words BROWN.
Colour the months of the year WHITE.
Colour the school subjects RED.
Colour the seasons BLACK.

Write here. The mystery picture is a ----------------------

Name the Days

Do you know the days of the week in English?
Can you fit them into the grid?

S S

Name the Animals

Name the animals and do the puzzle.

There is a message for a special day in the year. Which day, and what is the date?

The day is ______________________________.

It's on ________________________________.

The Pyramid Joke

Look at the pyramid. When you add up the numbers in two bricks that are next to each other, you get the number in the brick above them. Fill in all the numbers. Then find out what the joke is.

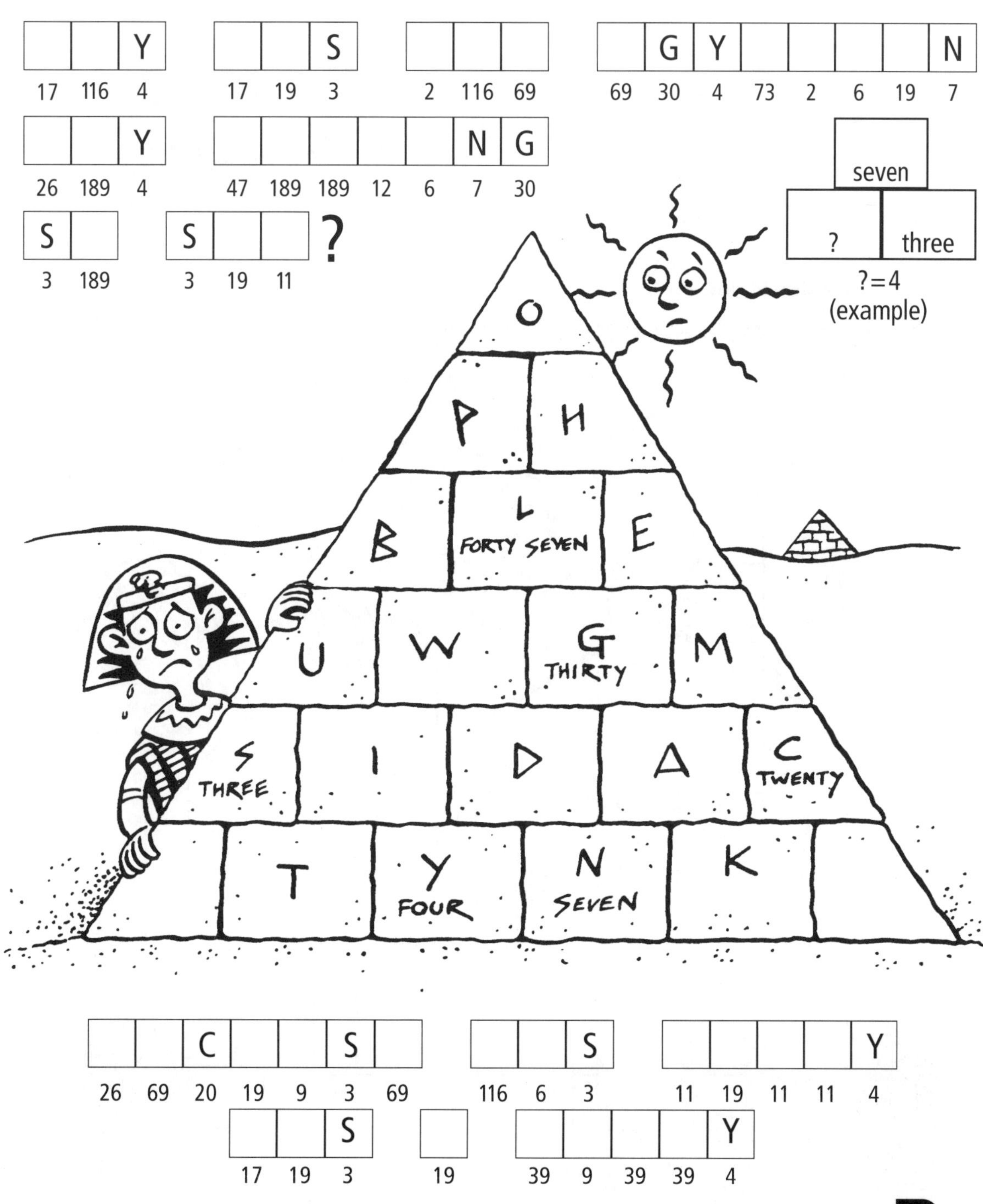

Find the Dogs

Can you find the dogs?
Match the people to the dogs.

1	2	3	4	5

Families

Read this and write the names in the spaces.

Mary is taller than Sue. Sue is next to Emily. Emily is older than David but not as old as Mary. Joe is between Mary and David. Molly is in front of Emily. Cathy is behind Felix and next to Robert. Cathy is the oldest. David is the youngest.

A = ____________ D = ____________ G = ____________

B = ____________ E = ____________ H = ____________

C = ____________ F = ____________ I = ____________

Now colour them.

Joe's wearing a red jumper and blue trousers.
Cathy's wearing a blue dress, a green hat and a yellow scarf.
Mary's wearing a green jumper and black trousers.
Sue's wearing orange trousers and a yellow shirt.
Robert's wearing a brown jacket, a white shirt and green trousers.
Emily's wearing a white T-shirt and purple shorts.
David's wearing a blue T-shirt and brown trousers.
Felix is black and white. Molly's grey.

Now draw Luke's family tree and put the right words in the spaces.

mother father brother sister grandmother grandfather

grandfather: *Joe* ____________ = ____________

____________ = ____________

____________ ____________ ____________ ____________

The Phantom Family Tree

Meet Wilma the Witch and her family. Write the names in the spaces.

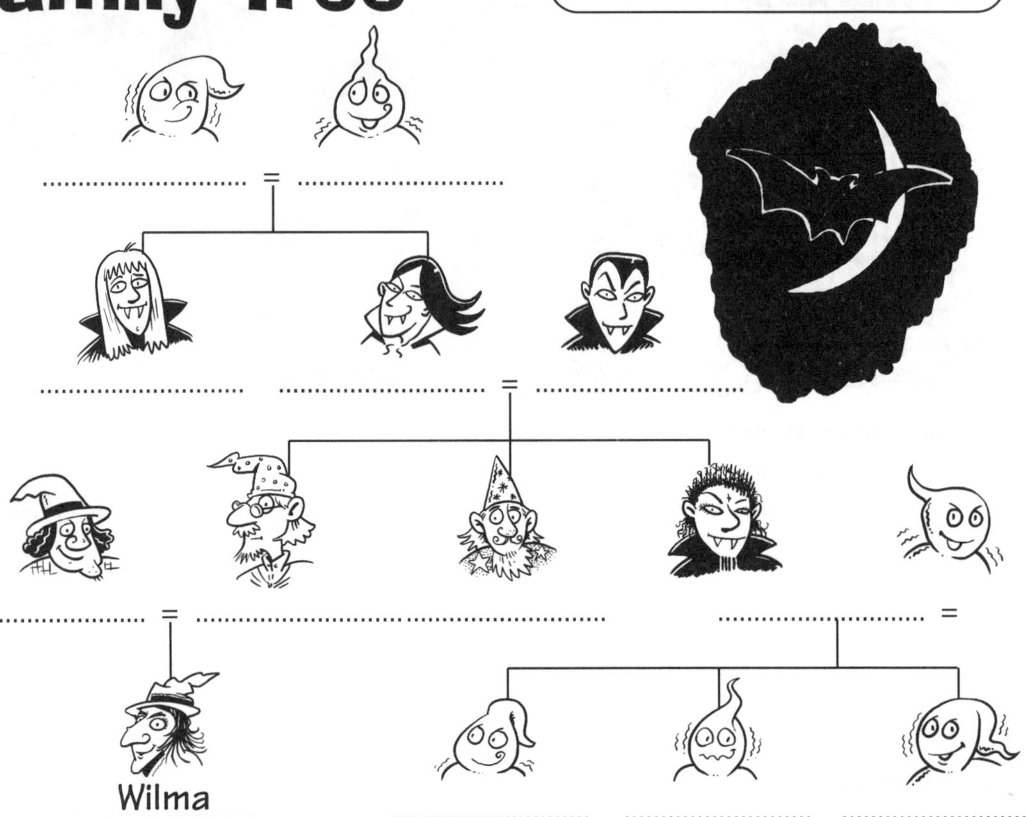

1. Wilma's father is called Willie the Wizard.
2. Wilma's grandmother (Vanessa the Vampire) is married to Victor the Vampire.
3. Godfrey the Ghost and his wife Gertrude are Willie's grandparents.
4. Wendy the Witch is Wilma's mother.
5. Walter the Wizard is Willie's brother.
6. Gertrude the Ghost's two daughters are called Veronica the Vampire and Vanessa the Vampire.
7. Victor the Vampire is Vanessa's husband.
8. Victor and Vanessa's daughter is called Victoria the Vampire. She is Walter and Willie's sister.
9. Gordon the Ghost is Graham's son.
10. Gary the Ghost is Gordon's brother.
11. Graham the Ghost is Gordon and Gary's father.
12. Gordon, Gary and their sister Griselda are Wilma's three cousins.

Hobbies

These people are talking about their hobbies. Find two things which belong to each person.

There are four things which don't belong to anyone. What are they?

____

____

____

____

Animal Puzzle

How much do you know about these animals? Answer true or false and follow the arrows to get to the end. The letters spell the names of two more animals.

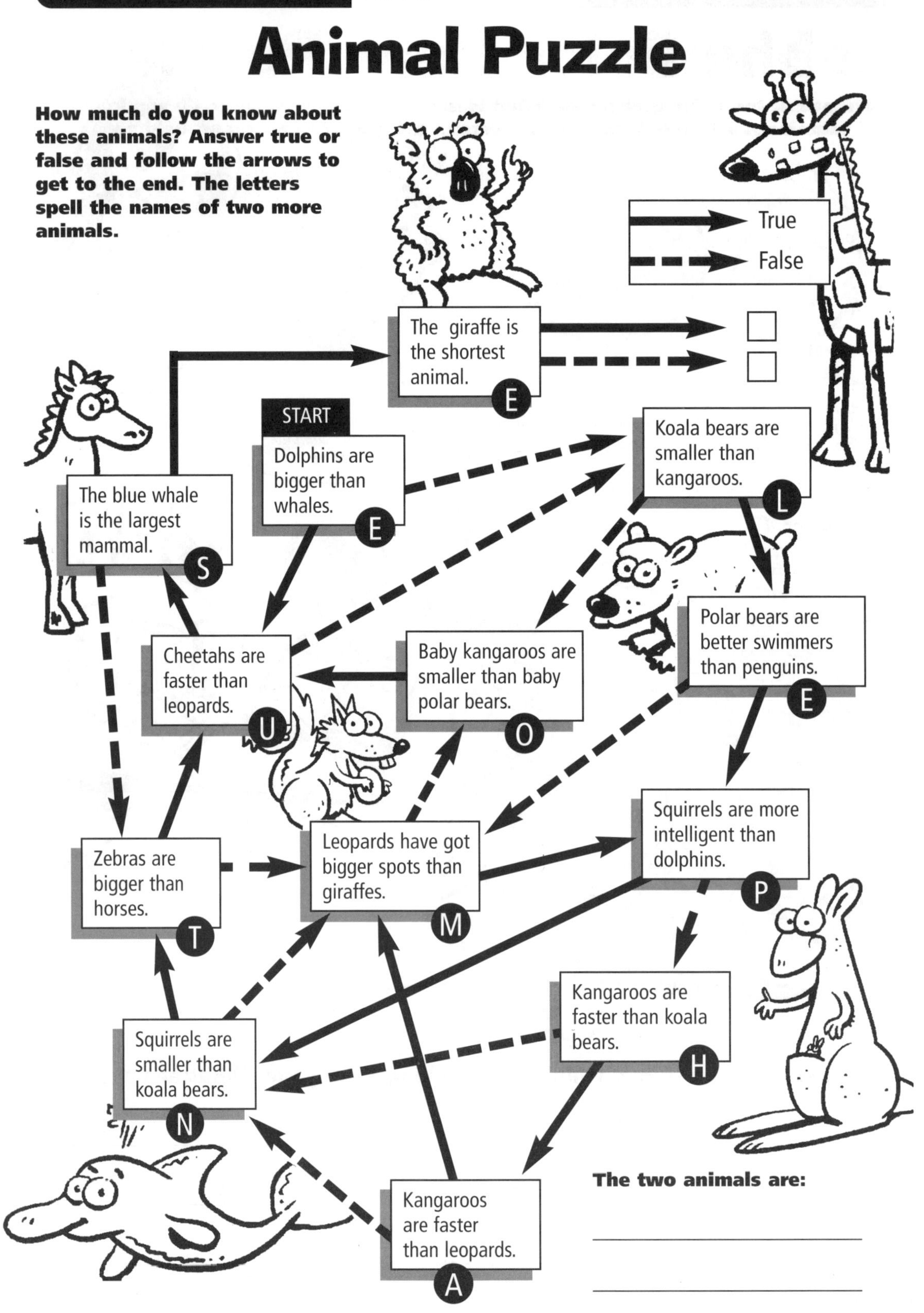

The two animals are:

____

____

The Polar Bear Puzzle

What can the polar bear smell? What is under the ice? How much do you know about polar bears? Write the answers in the grid. The anagrams help you.

1 The mother polar bear makes a hole under the ice for her ... . (siabbe)

2 Polar bears have ... under their feet. (riha)

3 A baby polar bear is ... when it is born. (nibld)

4 A baby polar bear hasn't got ... hair on its body when it is born. (yan)

5 A polar bear can ... at a speed of 10km an hour. (msiw)

6 A polar bear's ... is full of vitamin A. (vleir)

7 Polar bears like to ... Arctic foxes. (tae)

8 Polar bears often ... for up to 33 years. (vile)

The answer is in the shaded part of the grid.

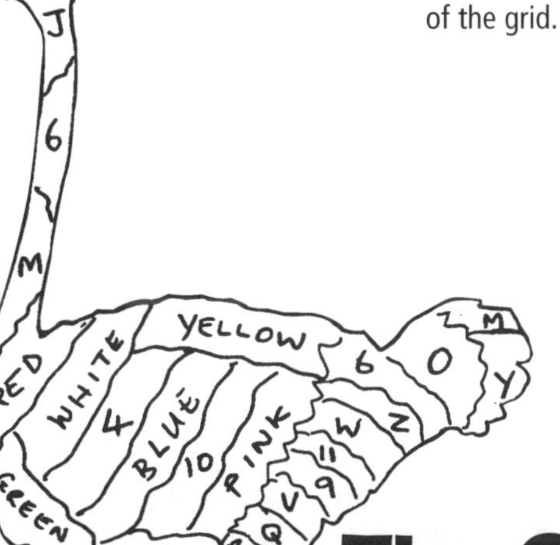

The Ostrich Puzzle

Ostriches lay very big eggs! How long does it take to boil an ostrich egg? Find out!

● Cross out the numbers between six and eleven ● Cross out the letters of the alphabet from H to N and Q to Z

● Cross out the colours. **The answer is ________ minutes.**

The Pet Shop

A **B**

Look at the two pictures of the pet shop and write down the 10 differences.

1. In picture A, a cat is fishing but in picture B a dog is fishing.

____

____

____

____

____

____

____

____

In Great Britain dogs and cats are the most popular pets. What do you think is the third most popular pet? Write the first letter of the names of each of these things and you can name the pet.

____

☐ ☐ ☐ ☐ ☐ ☐ ☐ ☐

Things Crossword

1			■	2		3	■	4 X		
	■	■	5	■	■		■	■	■	■
6					X				■	■
	■	■	X	■	■	■	■	■	■	7 X
■	■	■	8					■	■	
9	■	■	■	■	■	■	■	10	■	
	■	11		12		13				
	■	■	■		■		■		■	
	■	■	■		■		■		■	
14					■	15 X			■	■

Can you find all the missing things? Take the letters from the squares marked X.
You can find the thing which you need to help you get to school on time.

ACROSS

1 You can sleep in it. (3)
2 You can wear it on your head. (3)
4 You can drive to town in it. (3)
6 You can fly to America in it. (9)
8 You can cut things with it. (5)
11 You can talk to your friends in other towns with it. (9)
14 You can send a letter with this. (5)
15 You can open a door with this. (3)

DOWN

1 You can cross the river with this. (4)
1 You can drink this in England. (3)
5 You can read it. (4)
7 You can take photos with it. (6)
9 You can wear them on your feet. (5)
10 You can buy things with it. (5)
12 You can see in the dark with it. (4)
13 You can go for a walk in it. (4)

The mystery thing is a ___________

Find Ben

Where's Ben? Read about the dogs and find him.
Write the names by the dogs. What's Ben doing? Write the answer.

Holly doesn't like playing with the cat.

Max likes water.

Lucy likes playing the guitar.

Bruno, Jess and Oscar like playing with the Christmas tree angels.

Ellie likes eating bananas.

Lucky and Sophia like playing with the ball.

Barny, Bonny and Benjy like eating pizza.

Cassie likes skiing.

What about Ben?

Ben likes playing with the ______________________________

Clothes Rhymes

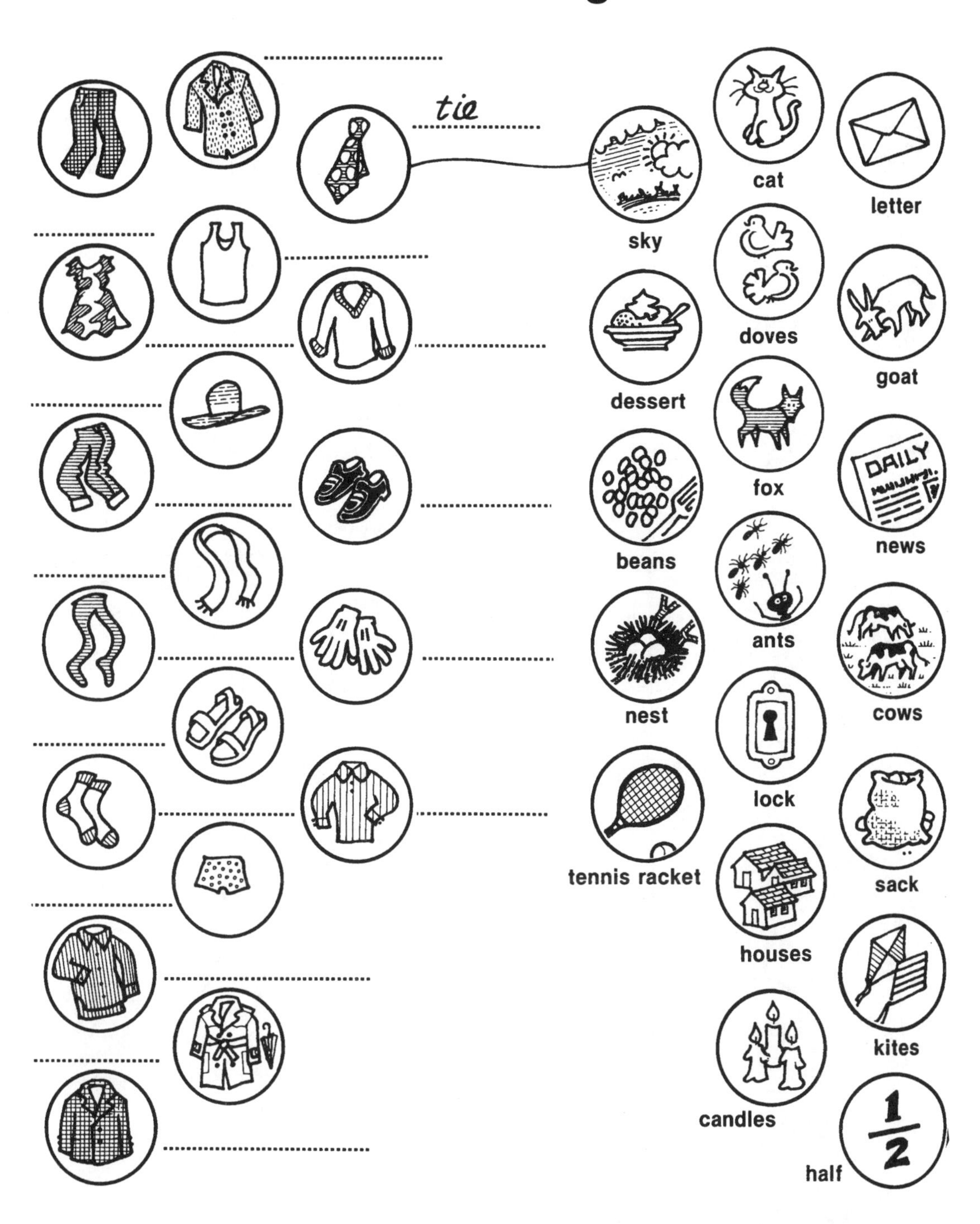

Do you know how to say the names of all the clothes on the left of the page? Look at the things on the right and find the words to rhyme with each of the clothes, for example, *tie* and *sky*.

Picture Crossword

Look at the pictures and write the words in the crossword grid

Clothes in Space

Write the names of the clothes next to the pictures. Look at the little numbers in the boxes. Put the correct letters from the boxes with numbers in the boxes at the bottom of the page. Learn a new fact about the planet Uranus!

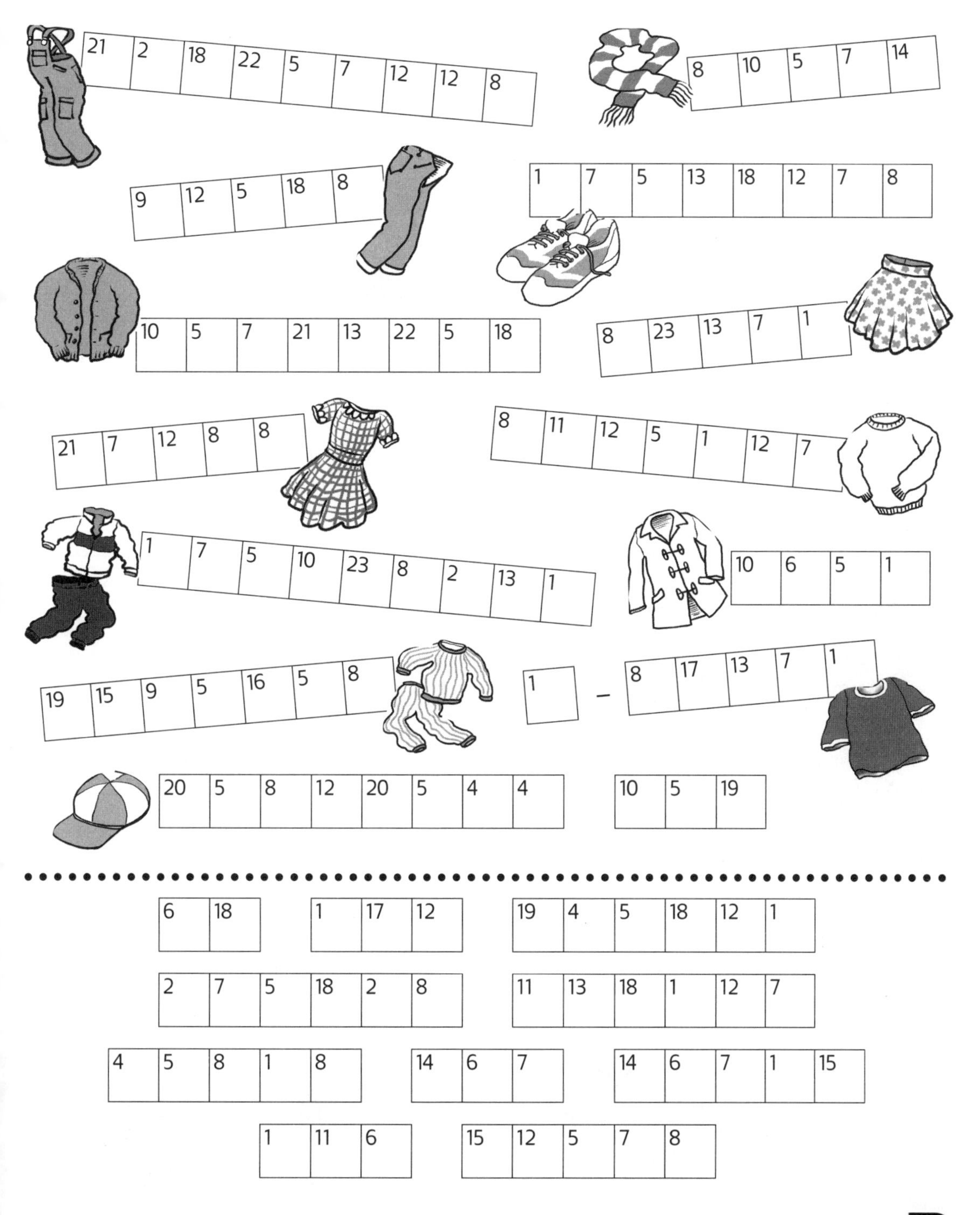

The Hat Shop

Put the sentences in the bubbles.

It's perfect!
It's too heavy!
It's too expensive!
It's too wide!
It's too old!
It's too big!
It's too tall!
It's too small!

Nature Watch

Look at these pictures for three minutes and then look at page 30.

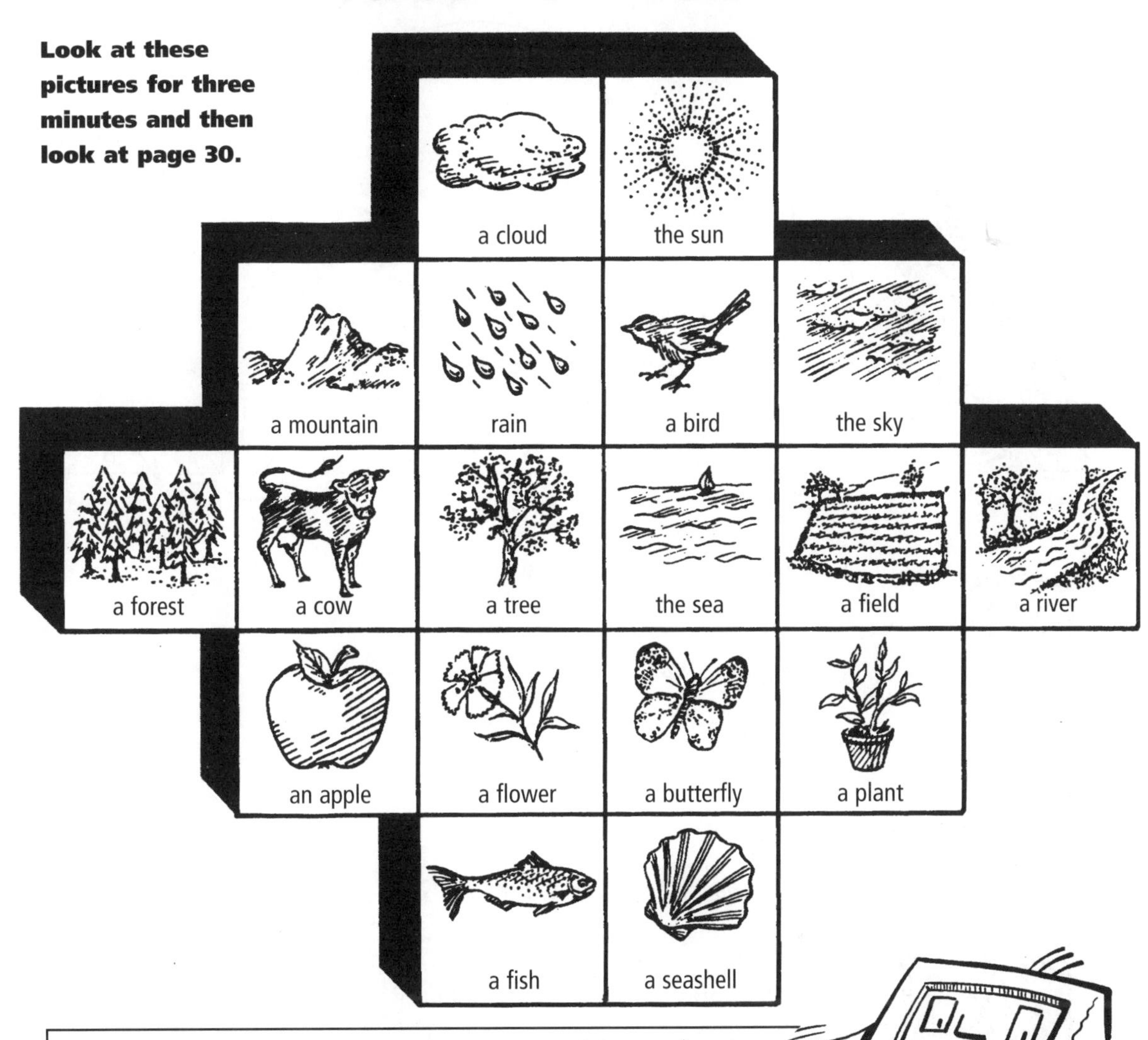

Can you speak 'Calculator'?

Can you understand your calculator when it speaks to you? Enter the number 0.7734 and turn your calculator upside down. What does it say?

Is your calculator happy or sad? Enter the number 334.334 and turn your calculator upside down. What's the answer?

Your calculator has got an English name. Enter the number 227. Multiply it by 2 and then by 17 and turn your calculator upside down. What's its name?

Is your calculator rich? What has he got in his pockets? Multiply 3319 by 16, add 600 and turn your calculator upside down to find the answer.

Nature Watch Memory Test

Now answer these questions.

1. How many pictures are there?

   ____

2. How many pictures of animals are there?

   ____

3. What is under the picture of the sun?

   ____

4. What is between the picture of the rain and the picture of the flower?

   ____

5. What is under the picture of the cow?

   ____

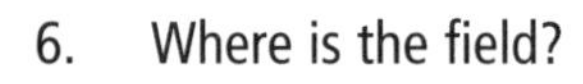

6. Where is the field?

   ____

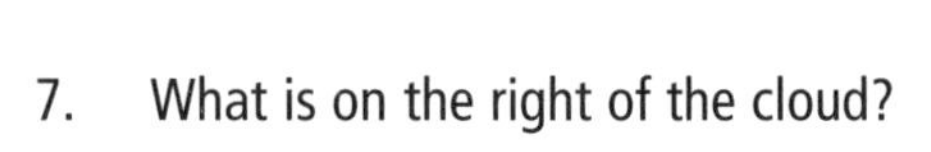

7. What is on the right of the cloud?

   ____

8. What is on the left of the seashell?

   ____

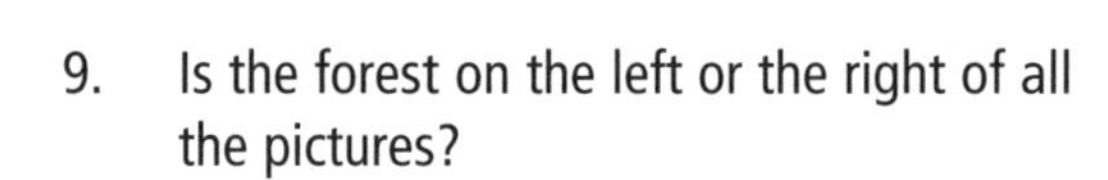

9. Is the forest on the left or the right of all the pictures?

   ____

10. Is the fish at the top or the bottom of all the pictures?

    ____

11. Where is the river?

    ____

12. Is the sky next to the bird or next to the flower?

    ____

The History Puzzle

The date is 980. The place is Britain. The Vikings are here.
Put the right word in each gap to make sentences.

ON IN UNDER BEHIND NEXT TO IN

The horse is ________________ the tree.

The dog is ________________ the river.

The baby is ________________ the fire.

The cup is ________________ the stool.

The book is ________________ the table.

The money is ________________ the bag.

Find 5 things beginning with C

1 ____________ 2 ____________ 3 ____________ 4 ____________ 5 ____________

Find 5 things beginning with B

1 ____________ 2 ____________ 3 ____________ 4 ____________ 5 ____________

Now cover the picture and see if you can remember it.
Put a mirror in front of the text below to see the questions.

How many trees are there?
How many dogs are there?
How many birds are in the sky?
What is on top of the house?
What's the weather like?

Choose one of these verbs:
cooking,playing,eating
What are the men doing at the back of the picture?
What are the women doing in the bottom corner of the picture?
What are the children doing in the middle of the picture?

What's the Weather Like?

1. Fill in the months on this calendar.

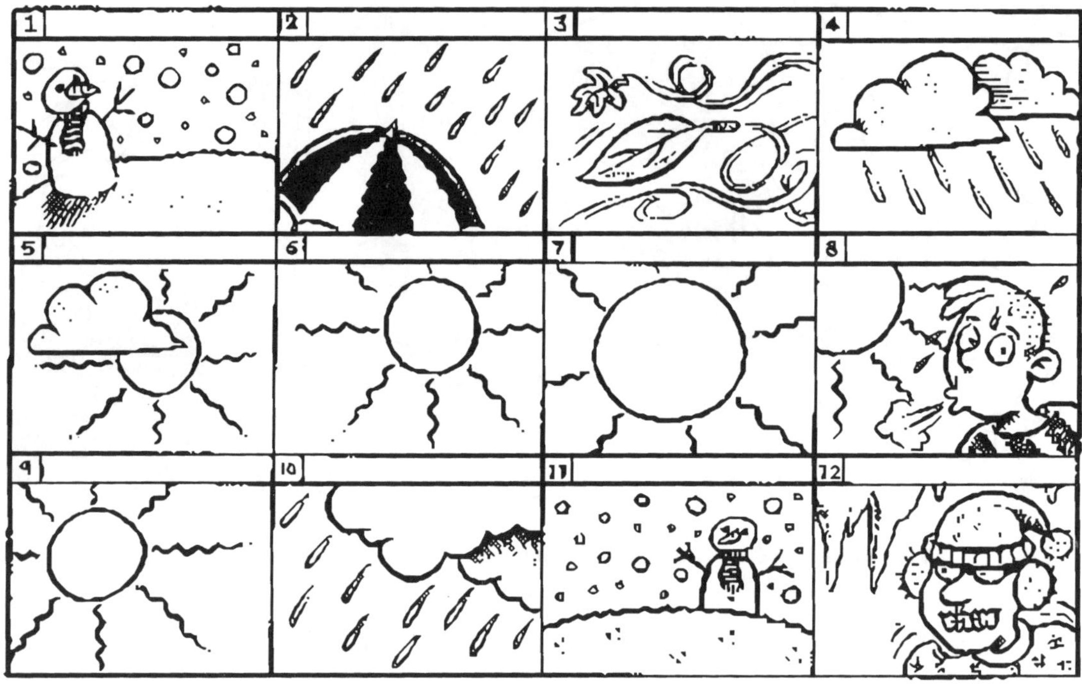

What's the weather like in July?
It's

____

What's the weather like in October?
It's

____

What's the weather like in March?
It's

____

How do you feel in December?
I feel

____

2. Look at these faces. How does he feel? Choose the right word.

SAD **TIRED** **THIRSTY** **HAPPY** **HUNGRY**

____

____

____

____

____

Answers

Page 5
Chase the Cheetah!
A cheetah can run at 97 km per hour.

Make a word
Great Britain + queen = green
egg + night = eight
cow + umbrella = comb
garden + page = a garage

Page 6
The Colour Circle
1) red, pink, black, white, orange, blue, brown, grey, cream, green, yellow, purple
2) 1 darker, white, lighter
2 lighter, darker 3 lighter, darker
4 darker, lighter 5 yellow, blue
6 yellow, white

Page 7
How many cats can you find?
There are 42 cats.

Page 8
Numbers and Colours

X	M	O	Q	T	W	O	F	I	C	E
R	B	N	L	U	J	V	O	X	T	L
P	E	I	G	H	T	P	M	W	R	O
K	D	N	B	I	H	C	N	U	N	W
H	O	E	U	M	U	Y	O	E	S	L
F	N	C	L	P	X	O	F	R	T	E
R	S	E	N	E	T	I	N	D	H	V
U	T	G	V	S	V	R	S	F	R	L
O	P	I	M	E	[illegible]	E	K	B	E	E
F	N	Y	I	J	S	T	N	D	E	W
W	L	E	F	O	S	N	G	E	L	T

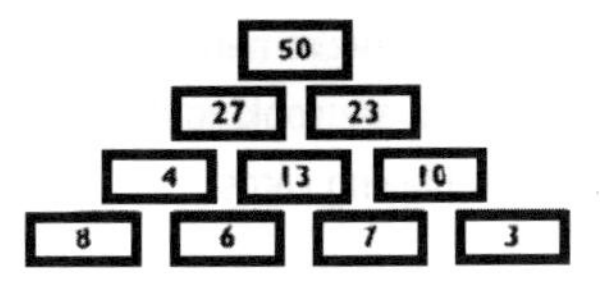

Page 9
Find the Treasure
The treasure is under the boat between the trees.

Page 10
Weekend Plans
1 swimming 2 cycling
3 shopping 4 video
5 football 6 park

Page 11
The Mystery Ship
The Mary Rose

Page 12
Make a sentence
Here are just a few possible sentences you can make:
The dogs are between the shirt and the elephant. I can see a hat. Here we are. Be careful Find that shirt. I can wear these jeans. His shirt is on that chair. How many dogs are behind the chair? An elephant is behind you. Don't look under the hat. She can see her dogs., etc.

Page 13
The Mystery Picture
To see the picture, turn the page so that the words are upside down. When all the sections have been coloured, it is a robin.

Page 14
Name the Days
Down: Sunday, Saturday
Across: Thursday, Tuesday, Friday, Monday, Wednesday

Name the animals
Hippopotamus, zebra, bear, rabbit, monkey, duck, chicken, kangaroo, pig, snake, cat, lamb, parrot, horse.
The message is Merry Christmas.
The day is Christmas Day. It's on December 25th.

Page 15
The Pyramid Joke
Why was the Egyptian boy looking so sad?
Because his daddy was a mummy.

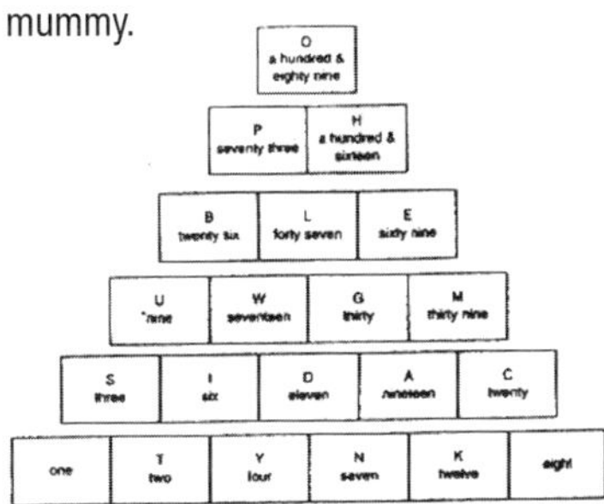

Page 16
Find the Dogs
1C 2F 3I 4G 5E

Page 17
Families
A = Joe B = Mary C = David
D = Robert E = Cathy F = Sue
G = Felix H = Emily I = Molly

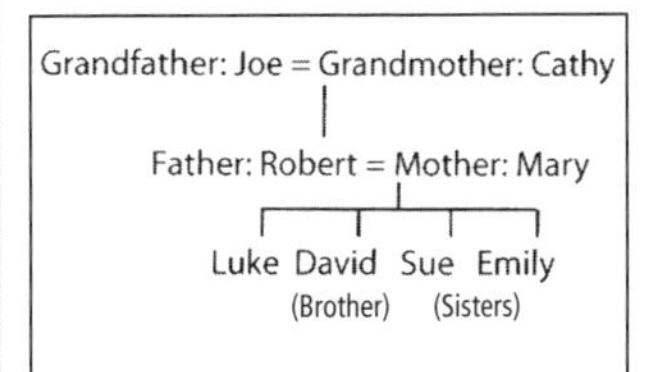

better than skiing for you.
14-18 = You are a skier but think about snowboarding; perhaps you can do it.
9-13 = Stay on your skis.
6-8 = Stay at home and enjoy a good video.

Pages 52 and 53
The Canada Quiz
1a 2a 3b 4a 5c 6b 7a
8c 9c 10c
The mystery Canadian is *Shania Twain.*

Pages 54 and 55
Down Under
1 false 2 false 3 true 4 true
5 true 6 false 7 true 8 true
9 true 10 true 11 true
12 true 13 true 14 true

Page 56
Rescue the Animal Lover
A young man climbed a tree to rescue a little cat. The cat climbed down but the man was too frightened to climb down. He waited in the tree for five hours until firemen rescued him.

Page 57
Punch Lines
1e 2a 3b 4i 5g 6f 7h
8c 9d

Page 56
Leo's Life
November, loved, drove, forty, been, hasn't, lost, his, will, want
The actor is *Johnny Depp.*

Page 60
The Pocahontas Story
1 became 2 had 3 lived
4 was 5 came 6 put
7 learned 8 caught 9 took
10 died 11 built 12 wanted
Pocahontas lived in *Chesapeake Bay.*

Page 61
The Native American Quiz
The false facts are 5 and 6.
The place is *Minnesota.*

Page 62
The Lion King
6-26 8-28 4-5 3-21
10-9 17-18 14-15 23-4
1-19 24-23 27-26 9-8
The word is: *help*

Page 63
The Boyzone Puzzle
7-21 14-19 38-8 1-14 2-16
11-25 9-28 3-2 22-1 5-3
17-33 8-17 18-15 15-30
39-13 33-9 34-35 23-11

Sports Wordsearch

**Write the names of the sports under the pictures.
Then find the sports in the wordsearch box.** ↓ → ↘

S	W	A	S	I	C	R	I	C	K	E	T
K	B	L	P	W	I	N	G	O	L	F	A
I	F	A	R	E	I	N	G	L	I	O	B
C	C	O	S	L	G	M	O	F	N	O	L
E	L	B	O	K	X	A	M	E	T	L	E
S	I	O	O	T	E	N	N	I	S	U	T
K	M	S	P	A	B	T	E	N	N	T	E
A	B	K	R	B	R	A	B	Z	E	G	N
T	I	I	U	L	P	U	L	A	N	O	N
I	N	I	G	O	L	X	E	L	L	I	I
N	G	N	B	A	S	K	Y	O	S	L	S
G	O	G	Y	M	N	A	S	T	I	C	S

The Party

What is everyone saying?
Find the correct words for each person.

(a) I'm sorry!

(b) Are you taller than me?

(c) Excuse me.

(d) What a pity!

(e) This is too heavy for you.

(f) It doesn't matter.

(g) Can I help you?

(h) Can you help me please?

Pancake Day

Do you know how to make a pancake?
Look at these 10 instructions.
Put them in the correct order.
Put 1, 2, 3, etc, by the pictures.

Put some of the butter in the frying-pan.

Toss (throw) the pancake.

Beat the eggs.

Eat the pancake.

Mix the milk and the eggs.

You need: 2 eggs, 1.14 litres of milk, 230g flour, 60g butter, a lemon, some sugar, a little salt.

Put one spoon of the mixture into the frying-pan.

Put some lemon and sugar on the pancake.

Add the eggs/milk to the flour/salt.

Mix the flour and salt.

Adopt an Animal

All of the animals are in danger. You can adopt an animal and take it home to live with you, but first, you must find out which animal is best for you, your personality and your habits. Do this test to find your ideal animal.

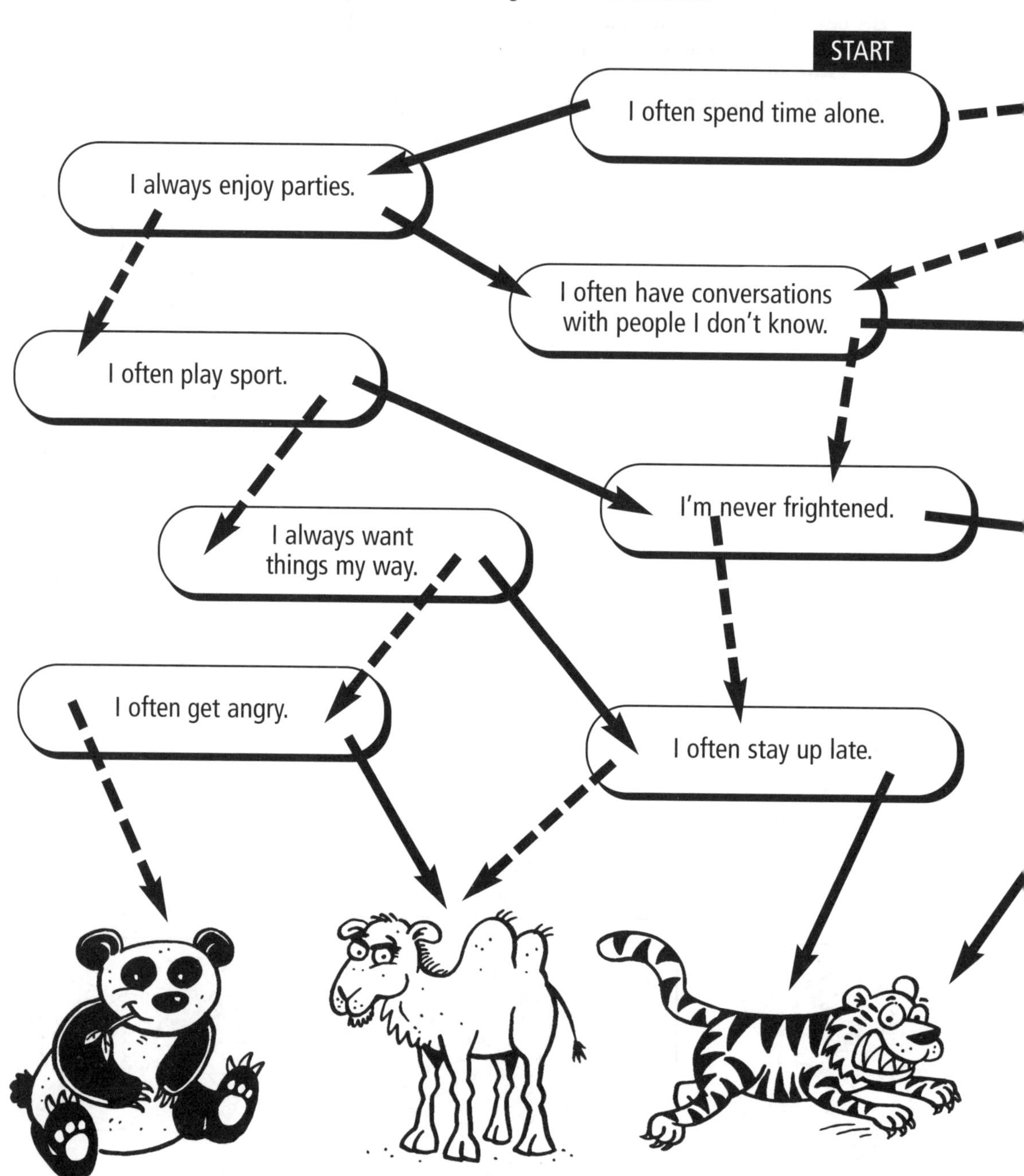

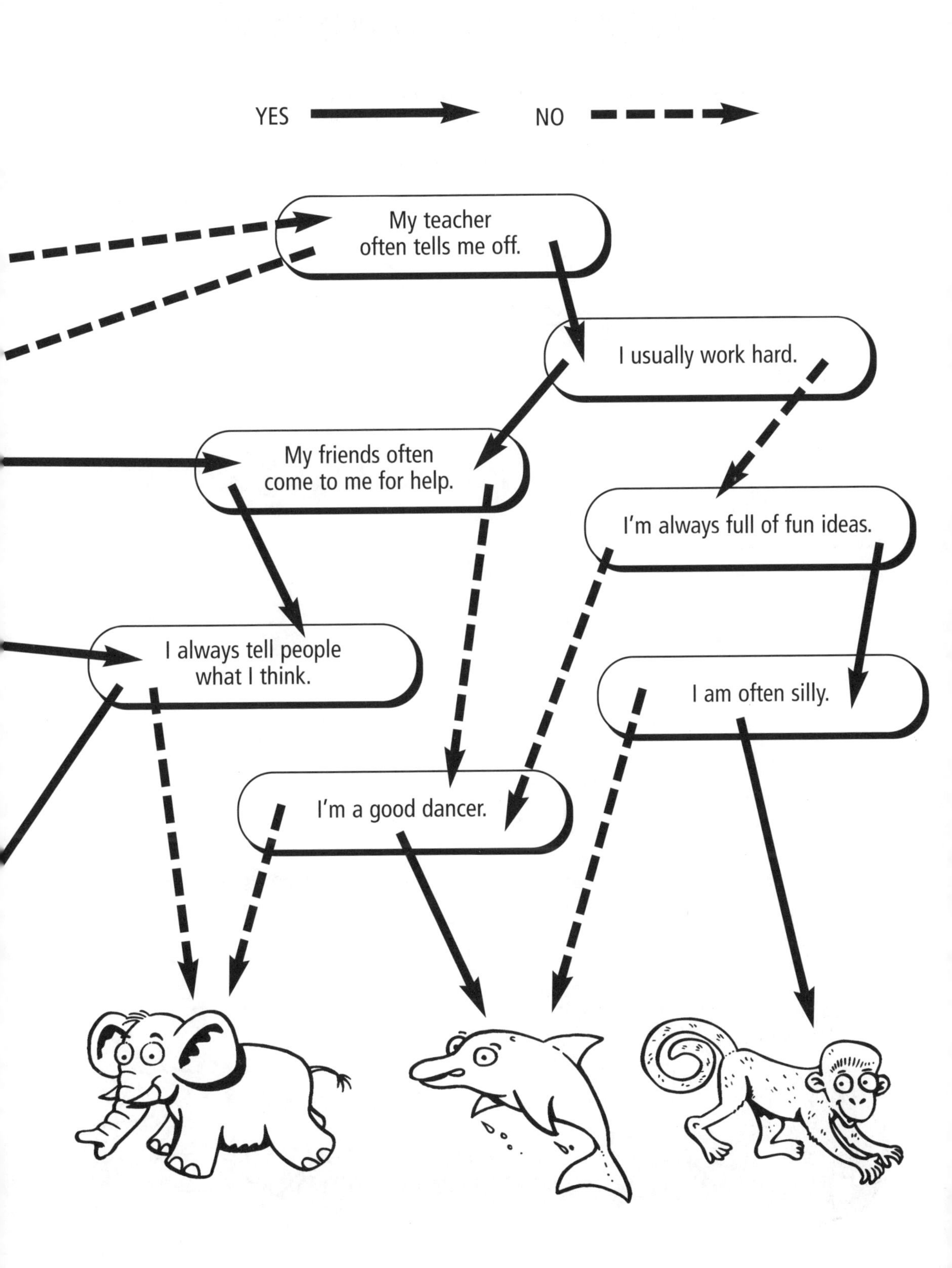
YES
NO
My teacher often tells me off.
I usually work hard.
My friends often come to me for help.
I'm always full of fun ideas.
I always tell people what I think.
I am often silly.
I'm a good dancer.

Animal Lovers Quiz

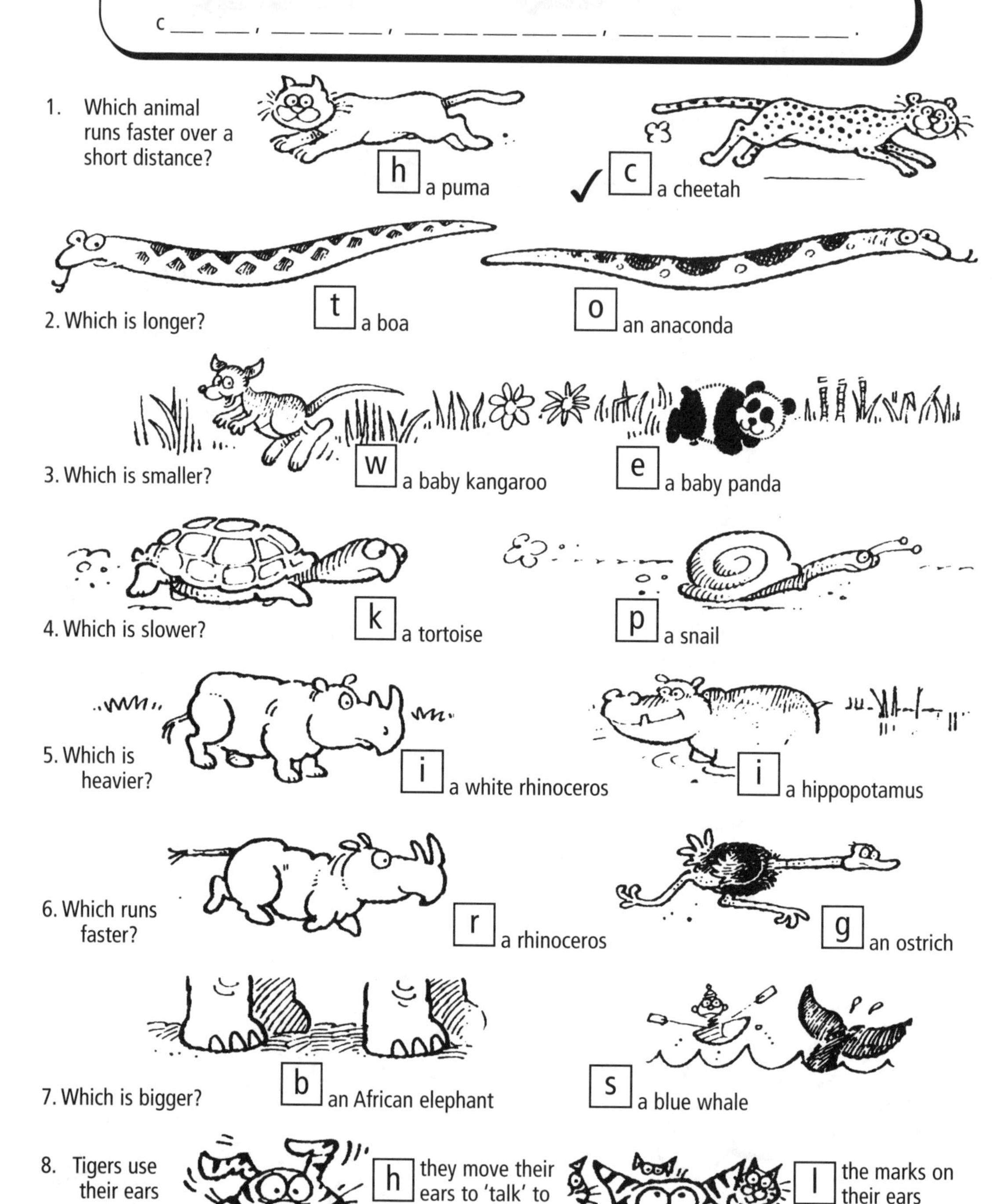

The correct answers spell the names of four farm animals:

c ___ ___ , ___ ___ ___ ___ , ___ ___ ___ ___ ___ ___ , ___ ___ ___ ___ ___ ___ ___ .

1. Which animal runs faster over a short distance?
   - h a puma
   - ✓ c a cheetah

2. Which is longer?
   - t a boa
   - o an anaconda

3. Which is smaller?
   - w a baby kangaroo
   - e a baby panda

4. Which is slower?
   - k a tortoise
   - p a snail

5. Which is heavier?
   - i a white rhinoceros
   - i a hippopotamus

6. Which runs faster?
   - r a rhinoceros
   - g an ostrich

7. Which is bigger?
   - b an African elephant
   - s a blue whale

8. Tigers use their ears to hear and
   - h they move their ears to 'talk' to one another.
   - l the marks on their ears show which family they come from.

9. How long can a sea lion stay under water?
m 10 minutes
e 30 minutes
s 4 hours
10. Which of these do killer whales eat?
e fish
e penguins
j people
11. How many litres of water can a camel drink in ten minutes?
w 20 litres
y 80 litres
p 121 litres
12. A rhino can
d hear better than it can see.
n see better than it can hear.
o see better than it can smell.
13. An emu attacks things
t with its beak.
b with its wings.
o with its feet.
14. Which lives longer?
c a flamingo
n a penguin
15. Which lives longer?
k a tiger
f a lion
16. Which lives longer?
r a zebra
e a rhinoceros
17. Which lives longer?
z a chimpanzee
y a camel

Big Cats

How much do you know about big cats?
Put these words into the text:

bigger *shorter* *smallest* *longer* *longest* *smaller* *faster*
bigger *rarer* *rarest* *biggest* *fastest* *longer*

Lions live in families. The males are b__________ than the females and they have l__________ hair on their heads. This hair is called a mane. Most lions live in southern Africa, but there are some in India. Lions sleep for about 18 hours a day.

Tigers live in forests in Asia, Sumatra and Java. Some tigers are b__________ than lions. Tigers are rare in the wild because people hunt them for their fur. Tigers live alone and hunt at night. They love water and can swim very well. **Leopards and jaguars** are very similar, but leopards live in Africa and Asia and jaguars live in central South America. Like tigers, they live alone. Leopards are s__________ than jaguars. Jaguars have l__________ tails. **Snow leopards** are the r__________ big cats. People hunt them for their fur. They live in high mountains in central Asia. **Cheetahs** are the f__________ animals.

Adjective Maze

The answer is always in the next square.

START	pink	blue	noisy	young	gold	interested	dead
small	grey	tall	quiet	beautiful	expensive	black	poor
hard	pretty	blonde	clean	light	green	rainy	horrible
silver	short	paper	square	heavy	yellow	easy	relaxing
funny	rich	cold	white	round	nice	good	slow
English	bad	fun	sunny	purple	frightening	small	red
fast	woollen	soft	Italian	stupid	crowded	sweet	wooden
FINISH	happy	French	long	interesting	clever	difficult	tidy

1 An elephant is this colour.
2 The sky is this colour.
3 A big party is...
4 The opposite of **old**.
5 The opposite of **ugly**.
6 Grass is this colour.
7 Opposite of **light**.
8 A shape with four equal sides.
9 Snow is this colour.
10 Nice weather.
11 You mix red and blue to make this colour.
12 Horror films are...
13 Ants are...
14 A tomato is...
15 Chairs, beds and tables are...
16 The opposite of **easy**.
17 Einstein was very...
18 The opposite of **boring**.
19 Pizzas and Pavarotti are...
20 This describes a party.
21 This describes people with a lot of money.
22 This describes the colour of some money.
23 This describes a good joke.
24 Queen Elizabeth, Mr Bean and Shakespeare are...
25 This doesn't describe a tortoise.

What does your picture look like?

- ☐ a fish
- ☐ an elephant
- ☐ a dog
- ☐ my best friend
- ☐ an alien
- ☐ a plant
- ☐ a house
- ☐ me

The Facts Quiz

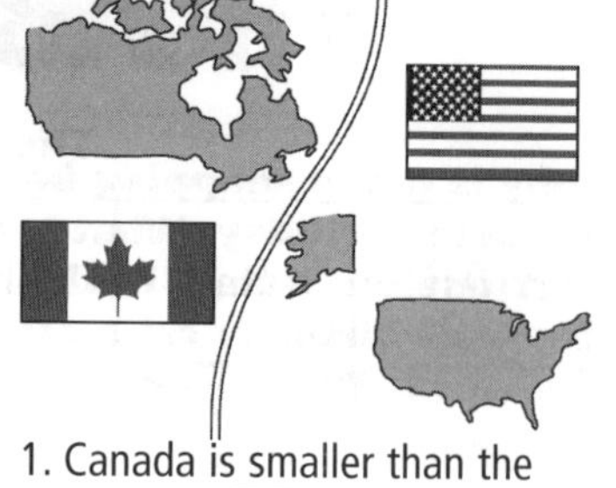

1. Canada is smaller than the USA. YES ☐ NO ☐

2. The London Underground (the Tube) is shorter than the Paris Underground (the Métro).
YES ☐ NO ☐

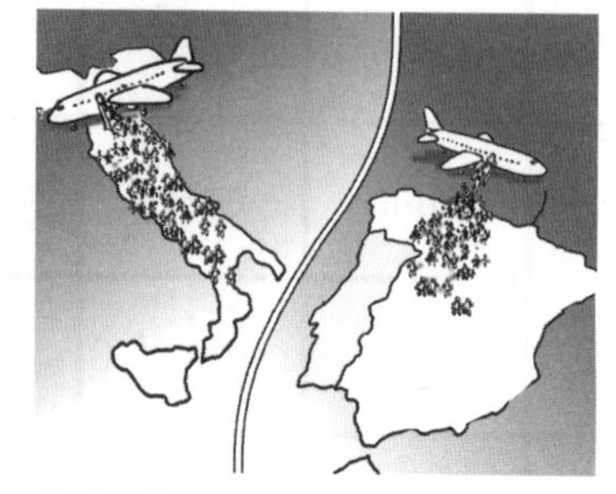

3. Spain attracts more tourists than Italy.
YES ☐ NO ☐

4. The Empire State Building in New York is higher than the Eiffel Tower in Paris.
YES ☐ NO ☐

5. The first computer is older than the first television.
YES ☐ NO ☐

6. Platinum is more expensive than gold.
YES ☐ NO ☐

7. Clint Eastwood is older than Jack Nicholson.
YES ☐ NO ☐

8. The Indian Ocean is bigger than the Atlantic Ocean.
YES ☐ NO ☐

9. Venus is bigger than Mars.
YES ☐ NO ☐

10. Jane Austen wrote more books than Charles Dickens.
YES ☐ NO ☐

The Birthday Present

Toby is going shopping because it's his mother's birthday. What is he buying for her? Use the letters in the squares with the little birthday cake candles to make the word. They are not in the right order.

ACROSS

1 In the sandwich bar you can buy things to take ...... or eat there. (4)

3 You can buy a pair of ...... and a scarf for the winter. (6)

5 "Have you got any trainers in size 6?", " ...... , I'm sorry, we've only got them in size 5." (2)

6 "Do you have any Japanese food?" " ...... , what would you like?" (3)

7 "I'd like some ...... to eat with my strawberries, please." (5)

9 "Can I help you?" "Yes, please, ... like to buy some sunglasses." (2)

10 If you want to buy some sports clothes, ... to the sports department on the ground floor. (2)

13 Always remember to say "please" and " ...... you" (5)

15 (See 8 Down) (2)

16 "Do you like the blue hat?" "No, ... doesn't suit me." (2)

18 "Have you got any of these T-shirts in blue ...... green, please?" (2)

19 (See 11 Down)

20 "I'd like some blue jeans, ..." (6)

DOWN

1 "Have you got ...... medium T-shirts please?" (3)

2 He/she serves you in a shop. (9)

3 Do you like to ...... shopping at the weekend? (2)

4 "I'd like ...... trainers, please." (4)

5 "Have you got any bananas, please?" " ...... I'm sorry, we haven't." (2)

7 "I'd like some potatoes because I'm going to ...... supper. "

8 (and 15 Across) When you want the assistant to help you, you say this. (6, 2)

11 (and 19 Across) "I'd like to ...... these trainers, please." (3,2)

12 " ...... you got any red hats, please?" (4)

14 "I'm ...... , we haven't got any trainers in your size." (5)

16 "You can buy a baseball cap ...... the sports department." (2)

17 "Excuse ...... !" (2)

The birthday present is a ☐☐☐☐☐☐☐☐

Supermarket Maze

Begin at the START sentence and follow the maze. If you think the sentence is correct, follow the black arrow. If you think the sentence is wrong, follow the white arrow. You will get out of the maze if you go to all the sentences once and make the right decisions.

11
Fred gave me a good advice about cooking pasta.
9
This fish is really delicious.
Finish
2
I want 2 bottle of Coke.
5
How about making a cake?
3
I asked her for a milk.
We need much eggs.
6

The Invitation Maze

Can you find the two paths through the maze?
Andy speaks first. Follow Andy's path in red and Lydia's path in blue.

START

Hi, Lydia. How are you? 9

Hi, Lydia. How do you do? 14

It was Thursday yesterday. 36

Fine, thanks. Thank goodness it's Friday. 300

Where are you? 15

Nothing, why? 600

Are you? 200

My name's Lydia. 400

I love going swimming on Wednesdays. 52

No. 12

Yes. What are you doing tomorrow? 5

That's a good idea. Let's go and see the new Leonardo di Caprio movie. 500

Sorry, I hate horror films. 75

That's a great idea. 150

I have to. 24

How about going to the cinema? 8

What a lovely day! 710

Would you like an ice cream? 180

How about seven? 75

Where's Martin? 150

Oh, no. I saw that last week. It was rubbish. Let's go and see Scream 2. 3

All right, forget the film. Let's go for a pizza. 5

That's a good idea. Give him a ring. 20

Where are you going? 9

How about toast? 7

All right. What time do you want to meet? 3

I don't think so. I hate it! 200

No problem. Why don't we invite Martin, too? 6

Thank you. 16

Here you are. Let's go. 94

I'm never late! 30

All right. See you on Saturday. Don't be late. 12

How? 63

All right. See you. 50

That's not true. 1

'Bye, Lydia. 4

'Bye, Andy. 5

How far is it? 210

Now add up the numbers on Andy's path to find out the height (in metres) of Nelson's Column (in Trafalgar Square) and add up the numbers on Lydia's path to find out the date of the Battle of Trafalgar.

Nelson's Column is ________________ metres high.

The Battle of Trafalgar was in the year ___________ .

Are You a Fish?

Most people love water (swimming, sailing, water sports) or just playing. But water is dangerous too and you must always be careful. Here are nine questions about water safety. Choose the answers and take the big letters under each one and write them at the bottom of this page. They make a new question and you can answer it.

1. At the beach what does the orange flag mean?

2. What is the best stroke to use if you want to swim a long way?

3. What must you remember when you go out on a boat in summer time?

4. Before diving you must always find out how deep the water is. What is the rule about this?

5. At the swimming pool what must you remember if you want to dive?

6. If you are windsurfing near a beach what must you remember?

7. What must you always wear when you go out in a small boat?

8. How long must you wait after a meal before swimming?

9. At the beach what does a red flag mean?

You must wait at least two hours after your meal.
T HOL

The sea is a bit rough and you must be very careful.
WHE

You must always wear a life jacket.
R NEX

You must not dive if the water is less than 10 metres deep.
U GOI

You must wear a hat. And don't forget to use sun screen because you burn more easily when you are on water.
RE YO

It's best to use breast stroke.
RE A

You must not dive when there are other swimmers.
NG O

Be careful! It's dangerous to swim. IDAY?

You must think of others and not get close to swimmers. N YOU

The question is: ______________________________.

My answer is: ______________________________.

Secret Message

Draw the times on the clocks.

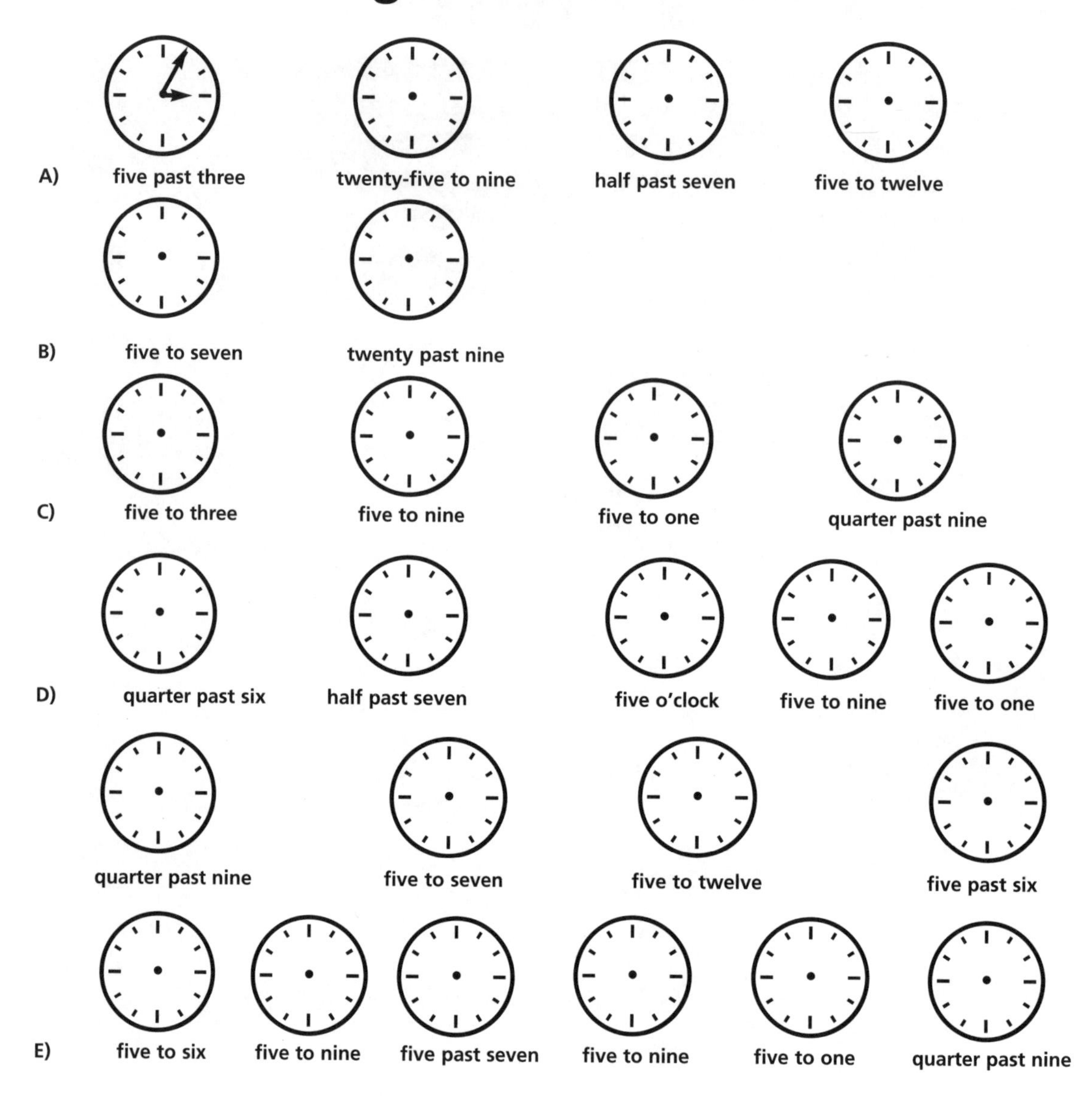

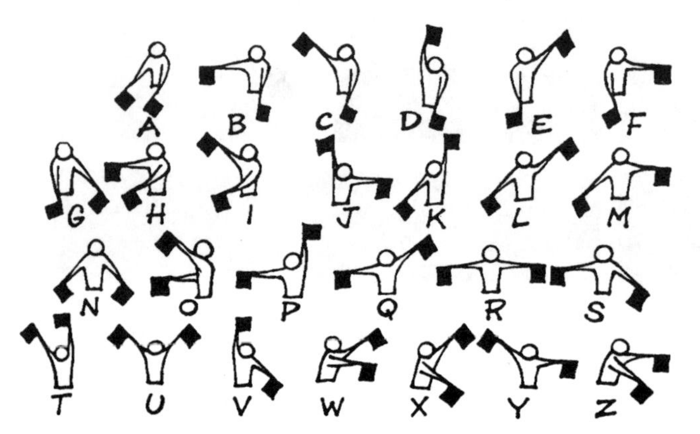

Now look at the semaphore alphabet. Find the letters which match the shapes of the hands on the clocks.

Write the secret message and give the answer.

A) W _ _ _ _   B) _ _

C) _ _ _ _   D) _ _ _ _ _ _ _ _ _ _ _

E) _ _ _ _ _ _ _?   Answer: ________

The Ice Skating Puzzle

Tara Lipinski was a world champion ice-skater when she was only fifteen years old. She was famous because she was good at doing triple jumps (three big jumps one after the other) in her skating routines. Triple jumps are very difficult. How many did she do in each dance when she skated in international competitions?

Do the puzzle and find out.
Match the halves of the sentences on the left to the halves on the right, then join the two numbers in the little box. Then you can see how many triple jumps Tara usually did.

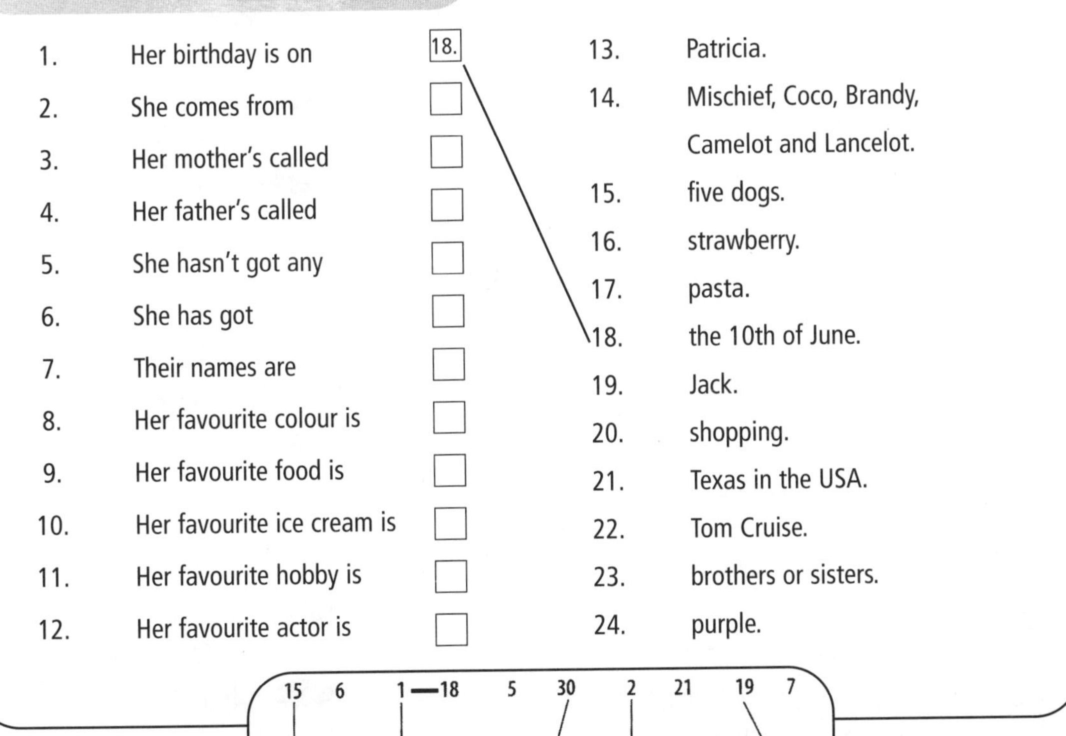

1.	Her birthday is on	18.	13.	Patricia.
2.	She comes from		14.	Mischief, Coco, Brandy, Camelot and Lancelot.
3.	Her mother's called		15.	five dogs.
4.	Her father's called		16.	strawberry.
5.	She hasn't got any		17.	pasta.
6.	She has got		18.	the 10th of June.
7.	Their names are		19.	Jack.
8.	Her favourite colour is		20.	shopping.
9.	Her favourite food is		21.	Texas in the USA.
10.	Her favourite ice cream is		22.	Tom Cruise.
11.	Her favourite hobby is		23.	brothers or sisters.
12.	Her favourite actor is		24.	purple.

The Ice Hockey Puzzle

Skate along with the ice hockey player and try to score a goal.
In each answer you have to change two letters in the previous answer.

1. Players often get ... because ice hockey is a violent game.
2. Ice hockey players have to work very ...
3. Ice hockey players wear helmets to protect their heads. Helmets are hard ...
4. The Maple Leafs are the Canadian team with the most ...
5. The puck is sometimes difficult to see because it move so ...
6. The Maple Leafs are the most popular team in Canada but they are not the ... players.
7. Eric Lindros is a famous ice hockey player; his nickname is 'The ... One'.
8. The Maple Leafs don't win many games. In other words, they don't ... many other teams.
9. Ice hockey players play between 82 and 102 games each ...
10. There are between 11 and 18 players in a ...
11. Wayne Gretsky is an ice hockey legend. He has more records ... any other player.
12. ... a player starts a fight, he has to stay off the ice for five minutes.
13. Top sports stars like Wayne Gretsky and Eric Lindros train every day of the ...
14. Ice hockey players have to ... harder than footballers.
15. You wear a thick ... inside your skating boot.
16. In ice hockey the 'ball' is called a ...
17. You ... the puck along with an ice hockey stick and try to score a goal.

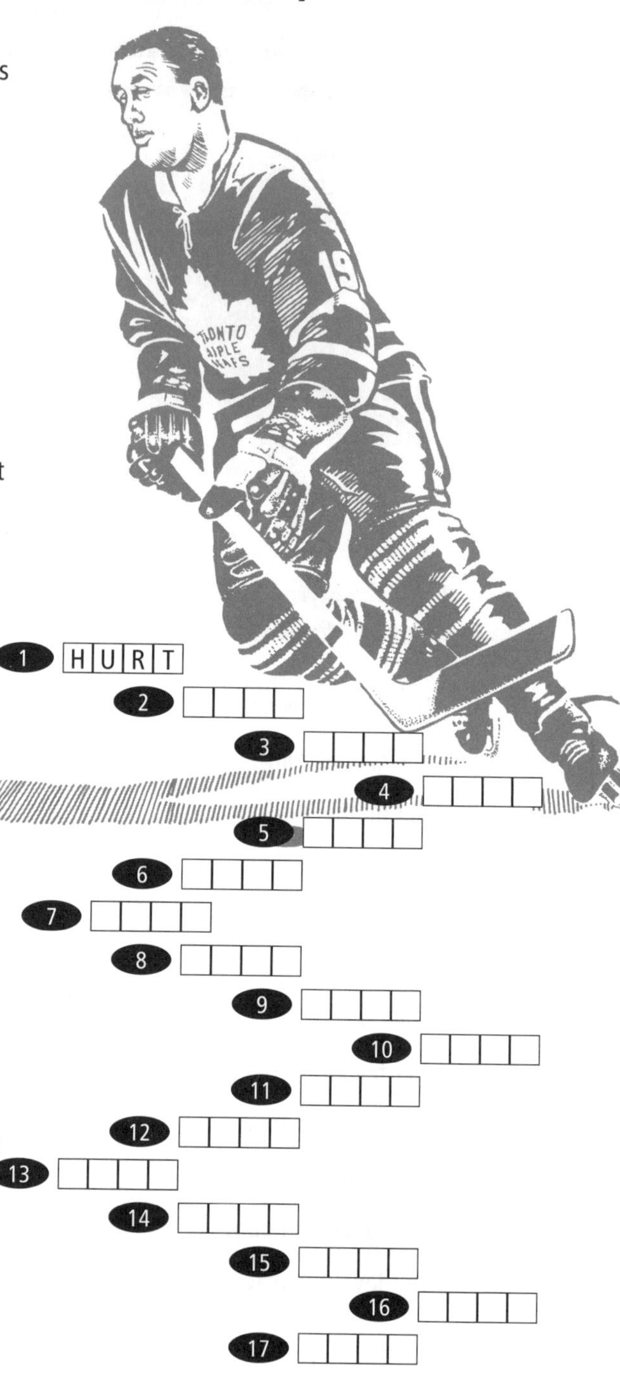

Snowboarding or Skiing?

Are you a snowboarder or a skier?

Which is the best winter sport for you? Do this test to find out. Choose (a) or (b).

1. You

(a) like to try new things.

(b) hate to try new things.

2. You think sport is

(a) serious exercise.

(b) good fun.

3. When there is snow on the mountains you think

(a) it's boring when your friends are not there.

(b) the world is silent and beautiful.

4. Danger is

(a) an important part of sport.

(b) bad in all sports.

5. It's important for winter sports clothes to be

(a) warm.

(b) fashionable and fun.

6. Speed is

(a) frightening.

(b) fantastic.

7. When it's snowing

(a) you get wet when you sit on the chair-lift.

(b) you don't notice the snow if you are having fun.

8. Falling over

(a) is annoying when you are out in the snow.

(b) is part of a winter holiday.

Look at the answer pages for the analysis.

The Canada Quiz

Answer these questions about Canada and some famous Canadians and find the name of a famous Canadian female singer.

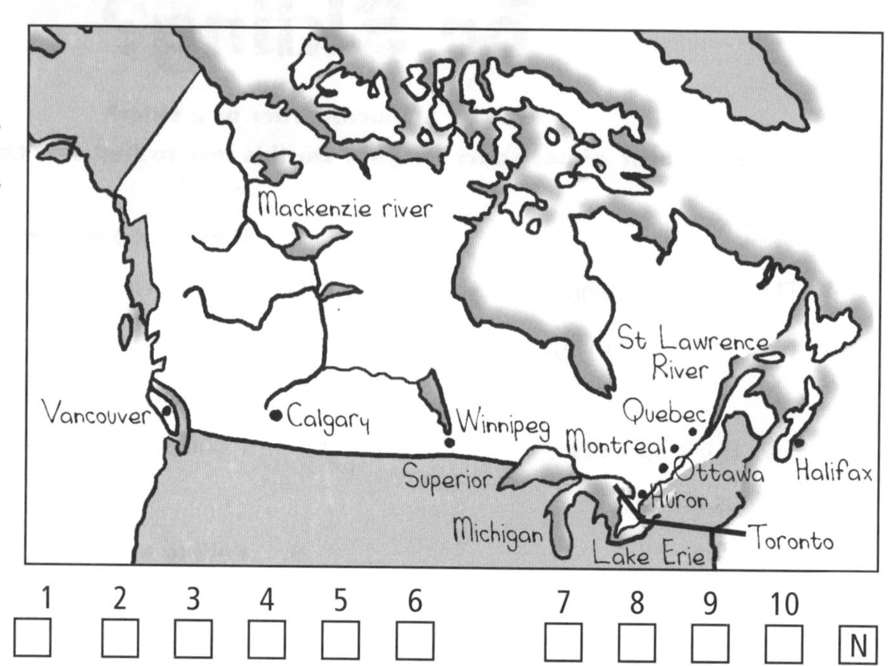

1	2	3	4	5	6		7	8	9	10	
☐	☐	☐	☐	☐	☐		☐	☐	☐	☐	N

1. Canada has two official languages. What are they?

(a) French and English - **S**
(b) Spanish and English - **E**
(c) French and Spanish - **T**

2. What is the capital of Canada?

(a) Ottawa - **H**
(b) Quebec City - **O**
(c) Toronto - **L**

3. What is the national symbol of Canada?

(a) The buffalo - **F**
(b) The maple leaf - **A**
(c) The polar bear - **W**

4. The Inuit people live in the north of Canada.

The words *kayak, igloo* and *anorak* are all Inuit words. What are the Inuit people often called?

(a) Eskimos - **N**
(b) Indians - **E**
(c) Aztecs - **G**

5. In many areas Canadians use special snow vehicles. What are they called?

(a) snowrides - **H**
(b) skilids - **O**
(c) skidoos - **I**

6. The east coast of Canada is 5,500 kilometres from the west coast.
How long does it take to go from Montreal to Vancouver by train?

(a) one day and one night - **K**
(b) four days and four nights - **A**
(c) six hours - **C**

7. Canadian money is:

(a) the dollar. - **T**
(b) the pound. - **P**
(c) the franc. - **U**

8. Which of these is not a Canadian river?

(a) the Yukon - **J**
(b) the St Lawrence - **V**
(c) the Colorado - **W**

9. Celine Dion is a famous Canadian. She was a Eurovision Song Contest winner in 1988 singing for

(a) France. - **E**
(b) Canada. - **B**
(c) Switzerland. - **A**

10. What's the name of the famous Canadian actor who was in The Truman Show and Batman Forever?

(a) Woody Allen - **N**
(b) Robin Williams - **F**
(c) Jim Carrey - **I**

Down Under

'Down under' is the English nickname for Australia.
Are you an Australia expert? Answer these questions and choose 'true' or 'false' and join the dots to complete the map of Australia. If your map looks like the correct shape, use an atlas to find out where these cities are:
Adelaide, Brisbane, Canberra, Darwin, Melbourne, Perth and Sydney.

	TRUE	FALSE
1. Australia is bigger than Europe.	1 - 5	5 - 13
2. A jumbo jet takes about 40 hours to fly from Australia to Britain.	7 - 27	7 - 11
3. Australia is 25 times bigger than Britain and Ireland.	17 - 27	7 - 27
4. Australia has seven states.	17 - 21	7 - 9
5. The capital of Australia is Canberra.	13 - 21	11 - 25
6. Sydney is in the state of Western Australia.	9 - 13	11 - 15
7. Sydney is bigger than Canberra.	17 - 29	17 - 23
8. Summer in Australia is from December to February.	5 - 9	7 - 13
9. Australians pay for things with Australian dollars.	5 - 25	7 - 15
10. The Aborigines are the original people of Australia.	7 - 29	15 - 17
11. The Outback is a large area in the middle of Australia.	3 - 9	3 - 31
12. Cattle and sheep farming is very important in the Outback.	1 - 3	1 - 9
13. There are ten times more sheep than people in Australia.	19 - 31	5 - 17
14. The east of Australia has more people than the rest of the country.	9 - 23	9 - 13

3
27
31
1
15
Northern
Territory
Western
Australia
Queensland
11
17
19
21
South
Australia
23
9
New
South Wales
29
25
7
Victoria
5
13
Tasmania

What's Your Game?

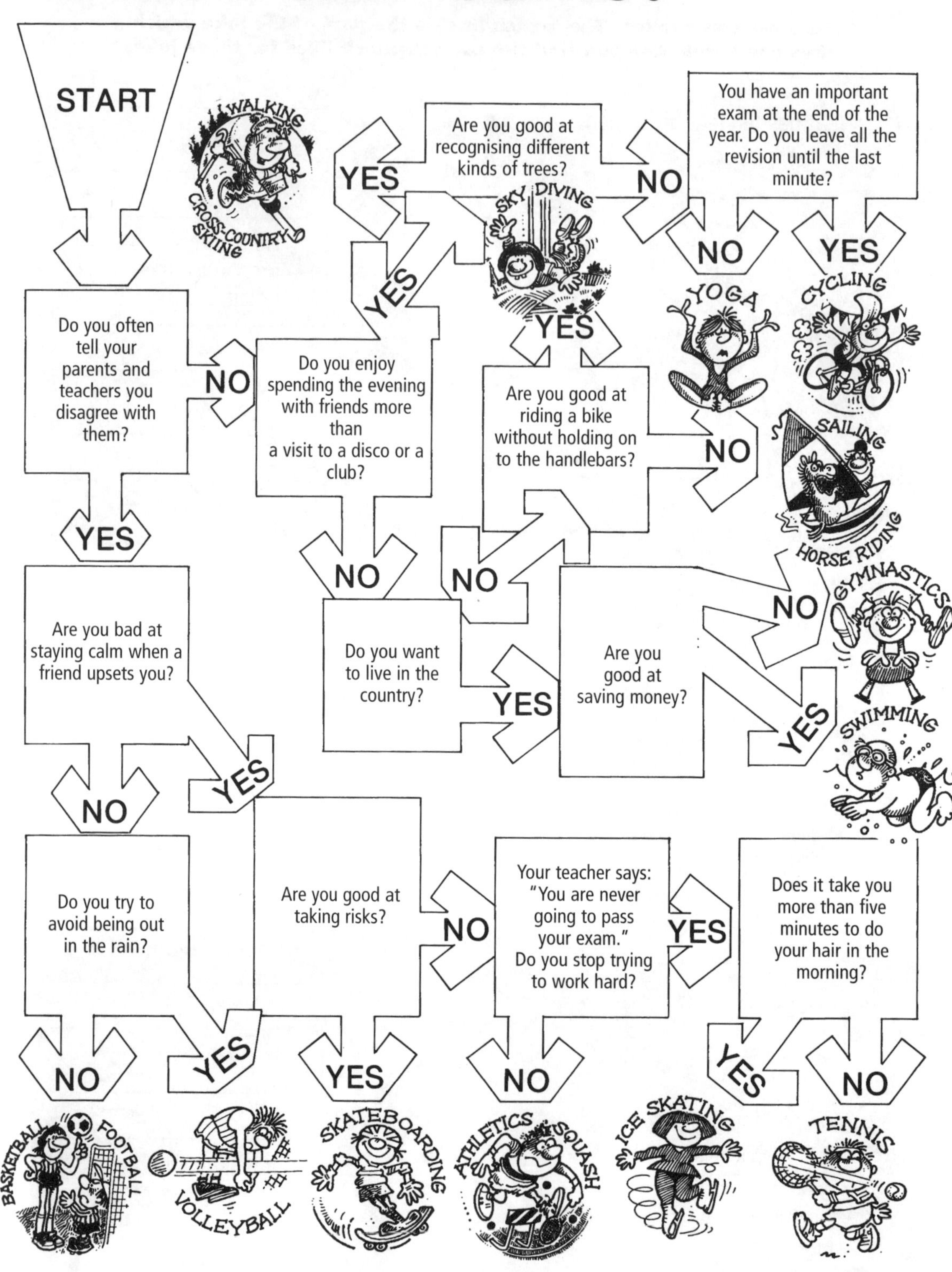

Punch Lines

Here are some jokes. The 'punch line' is the part of the joke which makes you laugh. Can you find the correct punch lines for these jokes?

1. What has ten legs, three heads and two tails?

2. What kind of dog has no tail?

3. Which question always gets the answer 'yes'?

4. Man: Doctor, I think I need glasses.

5. When can you say 'I is ... ' and not 'I am ... '?

6. How many seconds are there in one year?

7. What do you call a boomerang which doesn't come back?

8. Man: Doctor, I've got a problem.
I'm seeing two of everything.
Doctor: Lie on the sofa.

9. What's black and white, black and white, black and white ...?

a. A hot dog.

b. How do you pronounce the letters Y-E-S?

c. Which one?

d. A penguin rolling down a hill.

e. A man and a dog on a horse.

f. Twelve: January the second, February the second, etc.

g. "I" is the ninth letter of the alphabet.

h. A stick.

i. You certainly do! This is the bank.

Rescue the Animal Lover

There are some people who get themselves into trouble by helping animals. Help the fireman get to the top of the tree. Choose the correct word in each line so you can read the true story of what happened to the man and the cat.

Leo's Life

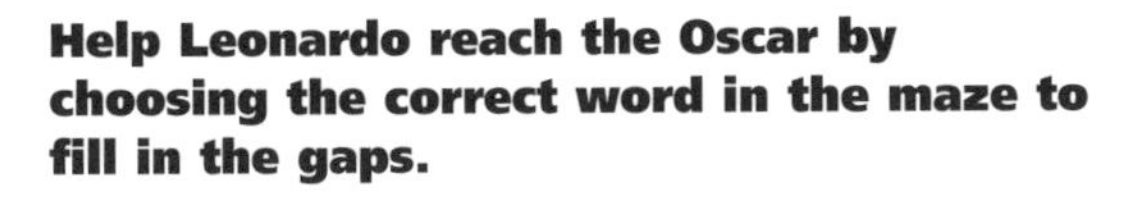

Help Leonardo reach the Oscar by choosing the correct word in the maze to fill in the gaps.

Leonardo DiCaprio was born on the 11th of ________________ in 1974 in Los Angeles. He grew up in a poor area of the city but his family ____________ him and helped him in everything he wanted to do. His mother ____________________ him in a car for two hours to get to a good school every day.

Leo started acting in commercials. He did thirty or ____________________ of them. After that, he did two TV series. He liked being on TV every week. Since then, he's ________________________ in films with some of the most famous people in Hollywood and now Leo is probably the most famous actor in the world.

His most famous films are *Romeo and Juliet*, *Titanic* and *The Beach*.

But Leo ____________ forgotten the most important things in life: family and friends. When Leo started to earn ________________ of money from acting, he bought _______________ dad a car. Leo says: "I have experienced lots of changes but I ______________ always be there for my parents. I _______________ to be the perfect child."

Leonardo won an Oscar for Best Supporting Actor in the film *What's Eating Gilbert Grape*? Find out who the main actor was in that film from the letters next to the words which you chose in the maze.

His name is ________________________.

The Pocahontas Story

Do you know the true story of Pocahontas?
Read her story and write the missing verbs in the boxes in the puzzle to find the name of the place where Pocahontas lived. (It's called Virginia now.)

Pocahontas (4) *w*__________ born in America in 1595. Her father's name was Powhatan. He was an Indian chief and he ruled a group of Algonquin tribes. In about 1607 the English (5) *c*__________ to the place where Pocahontas (3)*l* __________ . They (11) *b*__________ a town called Jamestown. Powhatan (8) *c*__________ a white Englishman. His name was John Smith. The Indians (12) *w*__________ to kill him but Pocahontas saved him. She (6) *p*_________ her head on top of his head. The Indians couldn't kill John Smith without killing Pocahontas. She was about twelve years old when she did this. Perhaps she (4)*w*__________ in love with him. John Smith went back to England without her. Later, in 1613, the white people (9)*t* __________ Pocahontas away from her family to live with them. She (7) *l*__________ English and became a Christian. She had a new name: Rebecca. She married a man called John Rolfe. In 1616 they went to England. When she was a young Indian girl in America she ran through the forest without shoes or clothes. In England she wore beautiful clothes and shoes; she met King James, and she went to big dances in London. When she was twenty-one, she (1) *b*__________ ill and decided to go home but she (2) *h*__________ to get off the ship in Gravesend, about twenty miles from London, because she was very ill. She (10) *d*________ in Gravesend and they buried her there at St George's church. Her son, Thomas Rolfe, went to Virginia in 1635. Perhaps you can find some of Pocahontas' family in Virginia now.

1
2
3
4
5
6
7
8
9
10
11
12
Y

The Native American Quiz

Pocahontas was a Native American.
The Plains Indians spoke different languages and had different customs but they all had a similar way of life. Read these facts about the Plains Indians and decide which are true and which are false. The letters will spell the Sioux Indian word for "cloudy waters". It's also the name of a place.

1. Plains Indian men didn't have much hair on their faces or bodies. If they did, they removed it.

TRUE M **FALSE** W

2. In tribes that didn't move around too much, men often looked after the children.

TRUE i **FALSE** I

3. Boys played a game that later became ice hockey.

TRUE N **FALSE** S

4. Indian camps always had a sweat room (sauna).

TRUE N **FALSE** C

5. Plains Indians never played gambling games and believed that gambling games were bad for the spirit.

TRUE O **FALSE** E

6. The parents of a baby chose its name six months after it was born.

TRUE N **FALSE** S

7. Eagle feathers were very valuable to the Plains Indians.

TRUE O **FALSE** S

8. The women put up and took down the tipis (tents).

TRUE T **FALSE** I

9. The Plains Indians had very clean white teeth because of their healthy, sugar-free diet.

TRUE A **FALSE** N

The Lion King

Kylie and Ben have been to see The Lion King at the theatre in London. Add the correct question tags to their conversation. There is a number by each empty space and there is also a number by each tag. Join the two matching numbers on the grid below and you can find out what to say when you meet a lion!

Kylie: It was brilliant, (6) 26 wasn't it?

Ben: Yes, it was even better than the film. The costumes were amazing, (8) ____________

Ben: They must have spent millions on them, (4) ____________

Kylie: I was quite young when the film first came out. We went with grandma and I was terrified of Scar, (3) ____________

Ben: I don't really remember. You weren't that young, (10) ____________

Kylie: I was seven. You tried to frighten me, too, (17) ____________

Ben: Only once or twice. You were too clever, (14) ____________

Kylie: I suppose so. I'm trying to remember the differences between the film and the stage version. They didn't leave any of the characters out of the stage version, (23) ____________

Kylie: No, I don't think so. Timon was in the film, (1) ____________

Kylie: Yes. What did you think of the music? It sounded incredible, (24) ____________

Kylie: That's because it was live. There's something really magic about the theatre, (27) ____________

Ben: But we'll still watch the film now and again, (9) ____________

Kylie: Of course! It's one of my absolute favourites. I'll never be too old to enjoy **The Lion King**.

18 didn't you?
15 weren't you?
26 wasn't it?
28 weren't they?
5 mustn't they?
21 wasn't I?
4 did they?
19 wasn't he?
23 didn't it?
26 isn't there?
8 won't we?
9 were you?

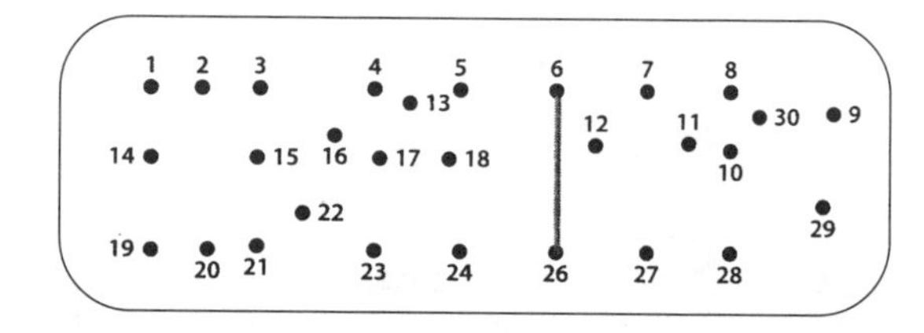

The Boyzone Puzzle

Shane Lynch is one of the members of Boyzone. He's got a pet called Caesar. Match up the questions and answers, then join the numbers to find out what kind of pet it is.

7 Shane's twin sisters belong to another famous pop group called ________.
14 Shane has got a tattoo of a ______ on his shoulder.
38 There are ________ boys in the group.
1 They come from ________.
2 Their names are _________ .
11 Ronan's nickname is _________ (just like the cartoon character).
9 Shane's hero is in his own family. His hero is _________ .
3 Keith has got ________ called Hugh.
22 Ronan likes eating _________ .
5 Stephen and Ronan have got the same star sign: _________ .
17 They've all got blue_________ .
8 Keith is a _________ .
18 Ronan's favourite sports are ________ .
15 They've got thirteen brothers and eight _________ between them.
39 Ronan is the _________ member of the group.
33 Keith was studying to be an _______ before he joined Boyzone.
34 If Mikey was on a desert island, he'd like to have _________ .
23 Stephen's birthday is on ________ , it's a special day in Ireland.

25 Tintin.
30 sisters.
14 Dublin.
21 B*witched.
17 father.
19 horse.
16 Shane, Ronan, Keith, Mikey, Stephen
28 his dad.
11 St Patrick's Day
2 a rabbit
13 youngest.
8 five.
35 his guitar, some sun-tan cream and a bottle of milk.
3 Pisces.
33 eyes.
9 architect.
15 golf and horse-riding.
1 pasta.

8 38 3 16 15 7 23 14 19

17 33 39 13 11 34 35

28 9 5 2 30 18 21 25 1 22

Material written by:

Caroline Ames-Lewis, **Phill Burrows**, **Marcus Fairs**,

Emma Grisewood, **Stella Martin**, **Paul Mellinger**,

Jane Myles and **Charlotte Stamford**

Project editor: **Judith Greet**

General editor: **Jane Myles**

Designers: **Clare Whiting**, **Christine Cox**, **Caroline Grimshaw**

Cover design: **Kaya-anne Cully**

Illustrations by: Keith Brumpton, Phill Burrows, Mark Burgess,
Abigail Carney, Chris Cox, Keith Hodgson, Keith Howard, Stuart Harrison, David Lock, David Parkins,
Andrew Warrington and Nick Abadzis
Photos by: Australian Tourist Commission, Canadian Tourism Commission, Epic, Gary M. Prior/Allsport, Digital Vision,
Walt Disney Pictures, Disney, Polydor, 20th Century Fox

Printed in the UK by Ashford Colour Press Ltd, Gosport, Hampshire